Downstream

John Bardach

Downstream:

A Natural History of the River

Harper & Row, Publishers
New York, Evanston, and London

Acknowledgments

Grateful acknowledgment is made to the authors and publishers who granted permission to reprint the following illustrations:

Fig. 2. Photo by H. Ambuehl, *Schweizerische Zeitschrift für Hydrologie*, 24: 353–484. Basel, 1962.

Figs. 3, 4, 16, 21, 22, 24, 25, 26 from Wesenberg-Lund, *Biologie der Süsswasserinsekten*, 1943. Available from Nordisk Forlag, Kopenhagen, and J. Springer, Berlin, Wien.

Figs. 5, 8, 9, 10, 11, 17, 20, 23, 35 from Robert W. Pennak, *Fresh-water Invertebrates of the United States*. Copyright 1953 The Ronald Press Company.

Fig. 14 from Illies, *Proceedings of the International Association of Theoretical and Applied Limnology*, Vol. XIV, 1961.

Fig. 15 after Franz Ruttner, *Fundamentals of Limnology*. University of Toronto Press, 1963. (Published in Germany by Walter de Gruyter and Co.)

Figs. 18, 19 from Justin W. Leonard and Fanny Leonard, *Mayflies of Michigan Trout Streams*. The Cranbrook Press, Bloomfield Hills, Michigan, 1962.

Fig. 36 appeared as cover photo, *Science*, Vol. 134, 14 July 1961, John H. Welsh.

Fig. 37 after Wiepkema, *Archives Neerlandaises de Zoologie*, Vol. XIV, 1961.

Figs. 38, 39 from G. E. MacGinitie and N. MacGinitie, *Natural History of Marine Animals*. McGraw-Hill Book Company, 1949.

Figs. 40, 41 from C. M. Yonge, *Oysters* (The New Naturalist Series). London: Collins, 1960.

Fig. 44 from Lagler, Bardach, and Miller, *Ichthyology*. John Wiley and Sons, 1962.

FIRST EDITION

LIBRARY OF CONGRESS CATALOG CARD NUMBER: 62-14596

Contents

Illustrations

Introduction

WATER IS FOREVER ON THE MOVE. IT POUNDS IN WAVES against the shore; it rises as mist and descends again as rain. In the soil it travels downward to feed the underground sources of springs and wells, and upward again through the roots and stems of plants. Even the glaciers of the high mountains are a part of the same cycle. But the most conspicuous of all moving waters are the streams.

There are the small forest brooks, flowing through deep shade broken now and then by a patch of sunlight—their waters clear as they tumble over a bed of small stones, or green with the reflected color of plants where the current is slower.

There are the fast streams, whose rapids and whirlpools and foaming cascades are witnesses to the friction between the water and its uneven bed. Fast, cool waters rushing down through valleys overhung by mountain peaks, through deep forests and open glades, invite you to pit your skill against them—to lure the trout that hide in their depths or to master their rapids in a canoe.

In the lowlands are other, gentler streams meandering through lush pastures, shaded here and there by an occasional elm whose branches overhang the water, and lending intimate charm to a landscape where man has worked long and patiently and where he still lives in harmony with the earth. Gathered in the broad curve of an oxbow are willow thickets and marshes that are the home of many water-loving birds and mammals. Hidden in the fertile water itself are countless other creatures, each adapted to its own place in the complex scheme of aquatic life.

Here and there the course of a stream is spectacularly broken by a waterfall—a silvery thread moving down the face of a cliff or a massive, thundering surge as at Niagara or Victoria Falls. Even here, though no creature can live in falling water, the moist places around the falls, the rocky overhang of the escarpment, and the torrent that forms below it, each has its own unique complement of plants and animals.

And there are the great rivers, such as the Mississippi, the Hwang Ho, and the Amazon, whose turbid waters carry silt washed down from the face of entire continents. Although they may look slower and lazier than their tributaries, this is often no more than an illusion, the result of their size. Watching the swirls of the current from the parapet of a bridge, with eyes fixed on one spot, you will be impressed by the speed with which a great river flows to meet the sea.

In the intricate shallows of the deltas and estuaries that are the meeting places of rivers and the tides, the miracle of life's emergence is believed to have taken place. Eons later, the first human cultures arose along the shores of rivers that are still routes of trade and migration, sources of power, and dispensers of life; for no creature on earth can live without water. By the same token a river can become a terrible enemy when it is swollen by floods, inundating the very fields and cities its life-giving waters have made possible. And as man has discovered, moving waters can also be abused to the point that they no longer perform the services he has come to expect of them.

Just as all these moving waters have their destination in the sea, their ultimate origin may be traced back to the same source. Water rises by evaporation from the oceans into the atmosphere, falls on the land as rain or snow, and finds its way back into the streams. Certain water molecules may be delayed at the surface; others go underground and reappear through springs; still others percolate into the soil, are taken up by plants, and evaporate once more through the minute pores of the leaves. The portion of the water vapor in the atmosphere that comes down as snow may be locked up for years or even for centuries in the ice of glaciers; but eventually, like all other water, it finds its way back to the sea in the never-ending movement of the hydrologic cycle.

Our knowledge of that cycle has evolved only gradually. The Greeks believed the sea to be the source of rivers, but supposed that it entered the ground through subterranean channels, to be purified and brought to the surface in the form of springs. Aristotle recognized the evaporation and condensation of water; Vitruvius, at about the time of Christ, noted that ground water gave rise to springs and had its origin in rain and snow. One of the many accomplishments of Leonardo da Vinci was to work out, at least in theory, the entire hydrologic cycle. But it was not until the twentieth century that even an estimate of the total volume of water involved in that cycle could be made.

That estimate is only approximate even now. But there are some figures, based on measurable data, that can be regarded as fairly accurate. For instance, it is agreed that the annual rainfall over the total land area of the globe amounts to approximately 23,900 cubic miles. The amount of water discharged into the sea annually is an estimated 6,000 cubic miles—the equivalent of about half the entire volume of the Great Lakes. The Mississippi-Missouri river system carries into the Gulf of Mexico a total of 410 billion gallons daily, or about a third of all the water that runs off the ground in the continental United States. Of all the river systems in the world, only the Amazon has a greater volume.

Throughout the world, the patterns taken by moving waters, from their mountain sources to their meeting with the oceans, show a notable similarity. The animals and plants of a glacial brook, or a mountain torrent, or a meandering lowland stream, will display certain typical adaptations in whatever part of the globe they may be found. The nature of these communities of living things will be a major concern of this book as it traces the downward journey of water on the move. And since man has formed the most conspicuous communities of all, the final section will be devoted to the part he has played—both for better and for worse—and that he is likely to play in the future.

PART I.

Headwaters

I

Glaciers, Torrents, and Waterfalls

MOST RIVERS ARISE FROM THE CONFLUENCE OF SMALL streams. Some, including such mighty thoroughfares as the White Nile and the Mississippi, arise out of lakes. Still others, including the Danube and many of the rivers of Florida, gush from the limestone of subterranean springs. Finally there are rivers like the Rhone, which emerges full-fledged from a glacier in the Swiss Alps.

Glaciers are found in all the high mountains of the world, as well as in the polar regions, and they all give rise to glacial streams. A glacier forms wherever snow accumulates in such quantities that it settles under its own weight. Then, compacted by further snowfalls, it gradually changes to ice. If the global climate were to become even slightly colder, snow instead of rain would fall in many places, and the size and extent of the world's glaciers would increase. If the climate were then to become moister, a large part of the globe would eventually lie under a mantle of ice. This is what happened during the epoch known to geologists as the Pleistocene, when ice sheets, which in places were more than 5,000 feet thick, covered nearly a third of the globe.

Since the last retreat of the ice sheet, less than ten thousand years ago, the climate has been sometimes warmer, sometimes colder, than at present. Europe had an optimum mild climate around 3000 B.C.; then it became colder again, and up until the second half of the nineteenth century glacier ice was forming faster than it melted (Figure 1). Today's mountain glaciers are but a small remnant of the ice sheets of fifteen or twenty thousand years ago; but they still demonstrate the force of moving ice, which has carved peaks like the Matterhorn, created countless lakes, and scoured out valleys such as Yosemite.

An accumulated thickness of 150 feet of ice on a mountain slope is enough to cause the ice to move downhill, carrying with it fragments of rock which have been broken loose from the mountainside by repeated thawing and freezing, and have become embedded in the ice. The movement of the ice, combined with the rasplike action of the broken rock fragments, bites away at the mountainside, grinding out a hollow depression or cirque, and thus a valley glacier is formed. Ice moves slowly, and to call a valley glacier a river of ice is only partly correct. Some of the apparent movement of glaciers is due to frequent shearing, breaking, and refreezing. Most glaciers in the high mountains flow at a rate of a few hundred yards a year, but they make up in mass and erosional force what they lack in speed. Transporting stones and debris as they advance, they build up moraines at their lower ends; these can become dams enclosing glacial lakes, which in turn may give rise to streams as water from the melting of the glacier at its lower edge seeks an outlet through the weakest point in the moraine.

FIG. 1 Aerial view of a retreating mountain glacier, the Gurgler Ferner in Austria. *1*, the glacial stream; *2*, *3*, and *4*, end moraines deposited in 1850, 1920, and 1953, respectively. Photo from Bundesamt für Eich und Vermessungswesen (Austria).

GLACIAL STREAMS

A stream may also arise directly from the melting of ice and snow at the glacier's surface. Water then percolates through the ice, runs off through crevices, and emerges at the valley end of the ice field, often through a large gate or archway. The heavy weight of the moving glacier grinds some of the underlying material to powder, and the resulting "rock flour" gives a milky appearance to the water of glacial torrents. But the valley end of a mountain glacier is usually flat, and the sediment unlocked from the ice by the melting process soon settles, making the stream crystal clear.

Glacial streams have daily and yearly water fluctuations; an early-morning low is followed by an afternoon high, and in summer some rivers, such as the Rhone, carry ten times as much water as in winter. This fluctuation in water regime also contributes to the formation of the archways of ice from which the water gushes forth. One might think that glacial streams would cease to flow completely during the winter; but even though both the air and the glacier's surface are frequently well below freezing, the friction caused by ice moving over rock releases heat enough to keep meltwater flowing continuously. Even on the Antarctic ice shelf one can hear the gurgling of glacial subsurface waters on most summer days.

Glacial Life

Even a glacier is hospitable to life. Certain algae, including some with red pigment (*Hematococcus*), have become adapted to withstand the glaciers' low temperature. The wind carries pollen from the conifers below, along with other organic debris, onto the ice; and when the sun warms their surfaces, glaciers provide not only a foothold for some primitive plant life but even a habitat for insects. The so-called glacierflea often occurs by the thousands on the lower reaches of a valley glacier. This is not a true flea but a springtail, a relative of another primitive insect, the familiar silverfish. Even in summer these glacial insects are subject to a wide range of temperature; the bright sun beats down on them during the day and they can be seen hopping over the ice in swarms, though they remain immobile at night when freezing temperatures prevail.

Adult glacierfleas live only a few months during the summer, subsisting mainly on the pollen that has accumulated on the ice. These scale-covered insects lay eggs that can withstand temperatures exceeding 60 degrees below zero. Their mastery of this rigorous habitat in turn makes existence possible for a predatory harvestman-spider, related to the daddy longlegs, that lives exclusively on a diet of glacierfleas.

Thus, even at the river's source, the glacier itself, a biological community embodying certain common principles of life which apply to all other communities is encountered.

Adaptation

All organisms have become adjusted to live in a specific habitat through the interplay of evolution and environment. Some are more tolerant of moisture, others of wide fluctuations of temperature, and generally each has arrived at its position in nature as a result of a long process of development, by minute steps, of specific organs and structures which fit the organism to survive under one certain set of conditions. Different forces are important in different locations. For the sparse community on the glacier's surface, the one overwhelming requirement is an ability to withstand low temperatures. Under less rigorous conditions are found animals with increasing variation in size, structure, and behavior—all of which represent adaptations to the temperature, to the amount of sunlight, moisture, and oxygen, and to such other variables as the speed of moving water, in a particular habitat. But in one respect all natural communities are alike: no matter how simple or how complex they may be, they are invariably tied together by a food web. This is a biological principle no less important than adaptation.

The Food Web and the Community

Essentially, any food web describes "who eats whom" in a specific environment. Thus, the predatory harvestman-spider of the glaciers depends for its existence on the glacierflea, which in turn feeds on the pollen that accumulates on the surface of the ice. Few food webs are as simple as this—or as the familiar formula, from grass to cow to man—but all are alike in being based on plant life. Only plants are equipped with the ability to capture the sun's energy by means of photosynthesis. Therefore their relative abundance determines the number of animals that can live in any one environment. The scarcity and the minute size of the plant life on the glacier are as important as surface temperature in limiting the size and number of its animal inhabitants.

In any aquatic community—whether in a stream, a lake, or the ocean—the plants are usually algae, primitive plants without flowers. Many of them are microscopic in size, or nearly so, as are most of the animals that feed on them. The largest animals in such a community, and therefore those of especial interest to man as food or as objects of sport, are usually predators and invariably the fewest in numbers—something to be remembered by anyone who wonders why there are so few trout in a favorite stream. All the organisms tied together in one food web belong to the same community—though food webs are usually intricate, with many cross-connections, so that communities often overlap. But even though the boundaries of a community cannot always be precisely defined, the system of the food web is self-contained, inasmuch as bacteria—often themselves the food of other creatures—break down what has been synthesized, making available the raw materials that enable plants to manufacture new sources of food energy.

The Glacial Stream Community

Though icy cold—rarely over 45° in summer—the uppermost reaches of a glacial stream harbor insect larvae, snails, and worms, as well as algae and scattered tufts of moss. During the winter the stream freezes over, except where there are riffles, and the cover of ice and snow insulate it both against further cooling and against evaporation, allowing animals to overwinter there. Though most glacial streams do not cease to flow in winter, they constitute an environment almost as rigid as the glacier itself, chiefly because of fluctuations in the amount and speed of the water they contain.

Nevertheless the glacial stream, like any other stream in mountainous or hilly country, offers a variety of habitats. Open, smooth, clear stretches of water with sandy bottoms alternate with deeper portions, overhung with borders of sedges and grasses; here and there in a protected place, an alder or willow takes hold. There are pools and riffles and large boulders left by the glacier, which dam the water, and in their lee are eddies and places where the water hardly flows at all. The riffles with whitecaps caused by stones and pebbles afford adequate aeration for the growth of algae; below riffles the water slows and cushions of moss and other plants appear, their fronds reaching far out into the stream. Then comes a small sill, almost a tiny waterfall, creating a still different set of environmental conditions. Water tumbling over such a sill travels hardly faster than six feet per second or five miles per hour, but at the bottom of a larger waterfall gravity and friction between water and stream bottom impart much greater speeds to the water —as high as 60 feet per second at the base of Niagara Falls.

Yet even small streams transport fairly large stones, and at a flow of three feet per second the water can carry a stone three inches in diameter, leaving bottoms of torrential streams with nothing but rubble and larger rocks, or occasionally with only bedrock. Water moving at a rate of about a foot per second can still carry particles of sand and rock fragments almost an inch in diameter. What lies on the bottom in an unobstructed portion of a stream will therefore be determined by the rate of flow of the water above it.

In any stream habitat the primary problem, for plants and animals alike, is that of obtaining a holdfast. Though animals also have the problem of finding food and of where to put or how to attach their eggs, coping with the force of the water is still the most crucial problem.

To understand the interplay of small stream creatures with their environment, one may begin by looking at the surface of a stream-swept boulder encrusted with green algae. Surrounding such a stone is a microscopic zone of molecular surface forces within which the water hardly moves at all (Figure 2). Depending on the temperature—the lower it is, the greater the viscosity of the water—the motionless boundary layer may be anywhere from a tenth to a thousandth of a millimeter thick. This measurement will determine the thickness of many rock-encrusting algae, to be found on submerged stones and ledges where the water breaks immediately above a fall.

While some algae solve the problem of holding fast in running water by staying minutely small, other plants seek a different solution: they live in small pockets of backwaters created by the turbulent flow. Still others, such as the water mosses and some larger algae of mountain streams, attach themselves with a holdfast to the thin algal mats. They grow long streamers that float in the water, like windblown hair; to reduce friction still further, many species have a slippery gelatinous external coat. So exacting is their adaptation to the high oxygen content of rapid streams that they are

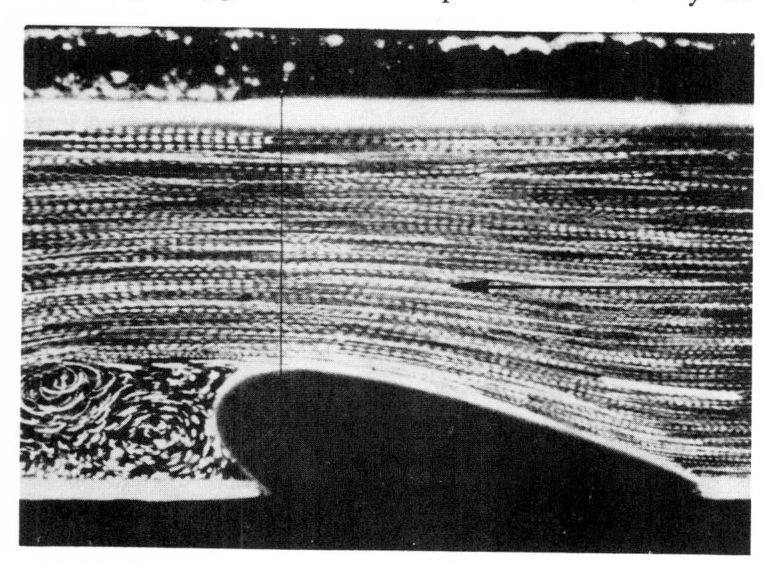

Fig. 2 Water flow over a stone in a mountain stream. Note even laminar flow above, eddies behind, and thin white layer on the stone where the water is slowed by friction. Photo by H. Ambuehl, *Schweizerische Zeitschrift für Hydrologie*, 1962.

often unable to survive after being transplanted into slower-flowing waters.

This minute underwater shrubland, which in its miniature fashion is as varied as any forest on dry land, offers protection to many animals. Others live in the lee of stones and boulders, and still others can brave the rapid flow. For the uppermost mile or so of a glacial stream, midge larvae are often the dominant animal form. They live exposed to the strong current on the surfaces of stones to which they anchor themselves by means of a cluster of chitinous hooks, borne on a pair of unjointed appendages called prolegs—quite different from the usual segmented legs of insects. The cluster of hooks resembles a multi-pronged grapple, and functions like one as it anchors the animal in the stream.

Midges (Tendipedidae) are a family of the huge insect order Diptera (a name from the Greek, meaning "two wings"), of which flies and mosquitoes are familiar representatives. Their larvae are to be found in almost all waters. Some are adapted to live in the bottom mud of lakes; others

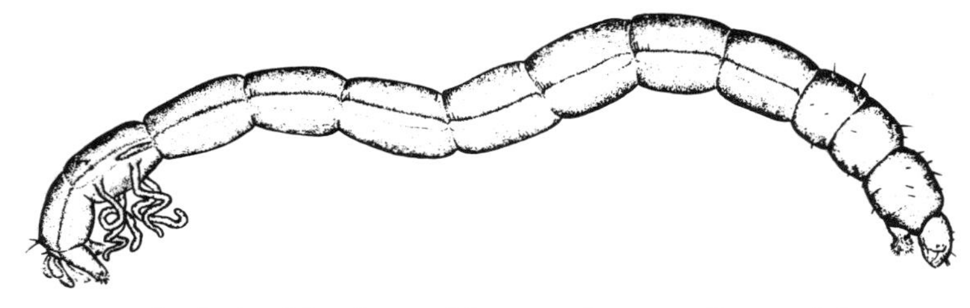

FIG. 3 Typical midge larva. Note prolegs on first and last segments, and coiled posterior gills. (From Wesenberg-Lund, *Biologie der Süsswasserinsekten*, 1943.)

burrow in the leaves and stems of water plants; still others are among the several animal indicators of polluted water; and most of them are important fish food. Some build cases of silk, others of lime; and still others hitch rides as symbionts on the larvae of other aquatic insects, or on the shells of snails. The larvae are slender, cylindrical, wormlike creatures, seldom more than an inch long. They have twelve body segments (Figure 3), and the different species range in color from white to yellow, green, blue, or pink; some are deep red, owing to a pigment dissolved in the blood. Like the human blood pigment hemoglobin this is an iron compound, and it functions in retaining oxygen when the air content of the water becomes low.

Larvae of another insect order, the stoneflies (Plecoptera), also occur in glacial streams. They are somewhat larger than the larvae of midges and are typically brown or green, often with prominent yellow and black markings. Their legs suspend the body from the side to give them better footing—rather than from below, as in most other insects. Usually hidden in nooks and crannies between stones, they sometimes come out and crawl about by advancing the fore and hind legs of one side together with the middle leg of the other, thus obtaining support and holdfast from both sides. The strong claws with which they grasp the stones are relatively larger in proportion to the size of the animal than those of a polar or grizzly bear.

Stoneflies and most other flying insects at the streamside have aquatic larvae and are bound to the water throughout the greater part of their life cycle. Adult stoneflies also stay close to the stream; they are poor fliers, and when disturbed they will drop to the ground to crawl rather than fly away. Though large and prominently veined, their two pairs of wings are thin. A pair of long movable antennae arises from the forehead, and the last abdominal segment terminates in a pair of additional appendages, the cerci, used in copulation but also serving as sensory organs. Both adults and larval stoneflies—which already show the cerci—look symmetrical because of these anterior and posterior "feelers" (Figure 4).

After the stonefly larvae leave the water to begin transformation into adults, they often have difficulties in finding nearby stones or debris rough enough for a secure anchorage while they molt. In such situations a transforming stonefly nymph has been observed to evert the chitinous lining of its own stomach and stick it to the smooth substrate. Thus anchored, the insect can safely split its larval skin, emerge, and then unfold its wings to dry.

Close to the glaciers in the coldest brooks of the Alps occurs a scavenging flatworm (*Crenobia*) of peculiar habits;

no comparable species has yet been found in North American glacial streams. Flatworms or planarians are usually only a quarter of an inch long; many, including *Crenobia*, have a sandy mottled color, and all have voracious appetites. They feed on wounded or dead animals, and infrequently on vulnerable insect larvae just after their molt. The food morsel is grasped by wrapping the head around it; then the mouth and pharynx, which are in the anterior third

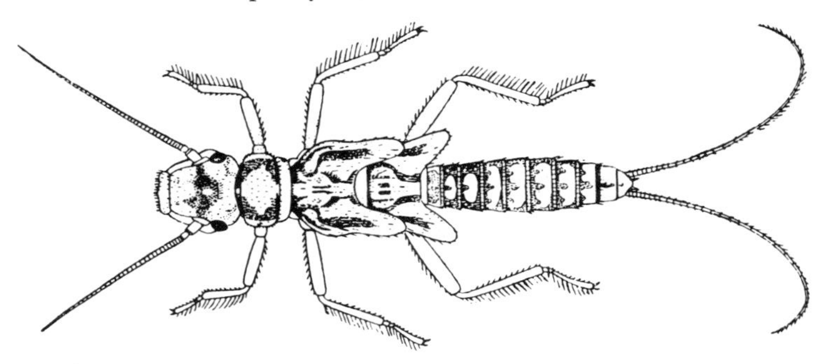

FIG. 4 Stonefly nymph (*Chloroperla*). (From Wesenberg-Lund, 1943.)

of the body rather than on the head, are turned inside out, and *Crenobia* eats itself through its prey. The worm moves by means of cilia that cover its entire body; as it glides over the stones, it is extremely sensitive to currents and temperature. Laboratory experiments have shown it to be so thoroughly adapted to life in icy moving water that when it is kept in still water it often cannot find its prey, which it locates by means of a chemical sense.

The very pronounced temperature preference of *Crenobia* is believed to indicate that the worm is a relic of the glacial period, when most waters of the Northern Hemisphere were as cold as the high mountain streams of today. It is assumed that as the ice retreated and the waters grew warmer, some southern forms of life replaced the ancient, cold-adapted animals which are now to be found only in a small part of their former environment.

If the glacial stream contains a sizable waterfall, it is not likely that any fishes will be found in its upper reaches. But if the way upstream is clear, or only slightly obstructed, trout are likely to come close to the glacier in quest of the insect larvae that colonize the stream bed. In the American and Canadian Rockies, high-mountain subspecies of the cutthroat and the rainbow trout (*Salmo clarki* and *Salmo gairdneri* respectively) can be found in open streams close to glaciers and snowfields. The trout, though, comes fully into its own after the stream has received several tributaries and has entered the tree zone below the glacial headwaters.

Animals of Torrential Streams and Waterfalls

The glacial stream receives smaller watercourses originating in high bogs and rock faces bordering their valleys. Water gushes through fissures and cascades down to meet the central stream. Other sources of water are from glacial lakes in hanging valleys, high above the valley floor; these often form waterfalls before they reach the bottom of the main valley. It is necessary to scramble up lower meadows in order to reach such cascades and to sample their fauna, which includes two peculiar groups of animals. One group is adjusted to truly torrential conditions, lives almost directly under the falls themselves, and has remarkable holdfast organs. The other group takes advantage of the spray and of the moist stones and swales in the vicinity of the waterfalls: it includes the so-called *fauna hygropetrica*, or "animals of the wet stones." Both groups consist primarily of insect larvae, although they do include some other animals.

A typical example of the first are the net-winged midges,

the Blepharoceridae. They would be recognized by few people and have not received a popular name, although they are widespread in the cold and mountainous regions of the Northern Hemisphere. The eggs, the larvae, and the pupae live in the water, and only for one month of the year do they emerge as the adult flying form—an inconspicuous,

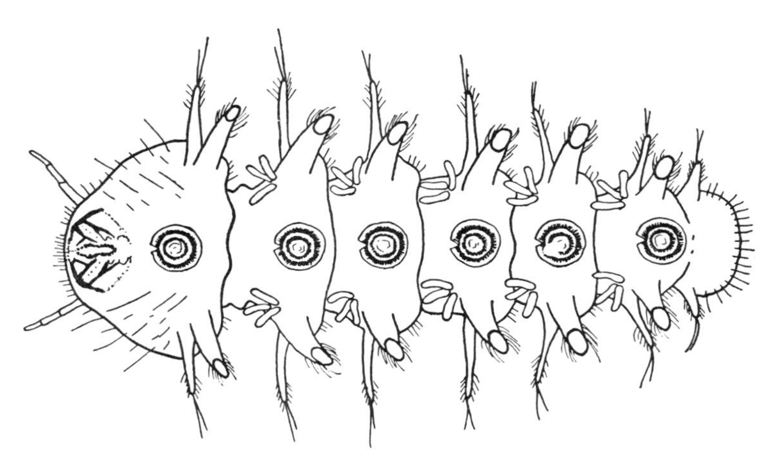

FIG. 5 Larva of a net-winged midge (*Bibliocephala*, fam. Blepharoceridae). (From Pennak, *Fresh-water Invertebrates in the United States*, 1953.)

middling-sized, mosquitolike insect that hovers by the streamsides.

The larva (Figure 5), slightly more than a quarter of an inch long, is flat and divided into seven segments. The first six of these each carries one of nature's most efficient holdfast organs. On the outside this organ bears a chitinous ring with radial grooves, whose center is a plug that can be raised and lowered through the play of the animal's muscles. Because the sucker muscles are at rest when the plug is elevated, a vacuum can be created with a minimum of effort. Adhesion is further improved by cement glands around the suckers, and by hairs which prevent any seepage of water between the suckers and the stones on which the animal rests. In addition to being good holdfasts for the larvae of the net-winged midges, the suckers also serve as a means of locomotion.

Unusual though these adaptations are, they but underscore the tendency of life to radiate into all possible environments. What is chiefly remarkable about them is the similarity of the holdfast mechanisms evolved by very different groups of animals. The surf zone of the ocean resembles mountain torrents in this respect, and in both of these life zones are to be found animals with strong claws, cement glands, suction discs, and suction cups. But spectacular as these attachment devices are, they are no more remarkable than the adaptations of other aquatic organisms to very different problems, which we shall encounter along the way from the headwaters to the sea.

2

Springs, Bogs, and Lakes

THE OCEAN IS THE ULTIMATE DESTINATION OF ALL STREAMS, and likewise precipitation gives rise to them all. The glacial brook derives its life from the accumulation of snow on the surface of the ground, but most other small streams come from springs, which in their turn originate as underground accumulations of rainfall and melted snow. Such accumulations of ground water, or aquifers, occur where there are porous layers of soil or rock with impervious layers below, and sometimes above as well. In mountainous regions these layers are often more tilted than in the plains, forcing the underground water to move downhill, sometimes for considerable distances.

The composition of an aquifer determines its capacity: coarse sand, for example, may store up to three gallons of water per cubic foot, limestone not more than half a gallon. The composition and the slant of the porous layer together determine the rate at which the water travels; this may be anywhere from a few inches to a hundred yards a day. Wherever the formation of the earth's crust is such that the aquifer and its underlying layer of impervious soil or rock come to the surface, a spring is produced. This may occur, for example, where there is a fissure in an impermeable overlying layer, or where the geological strata have been tilted upward (Figure 6). In more level areas, the

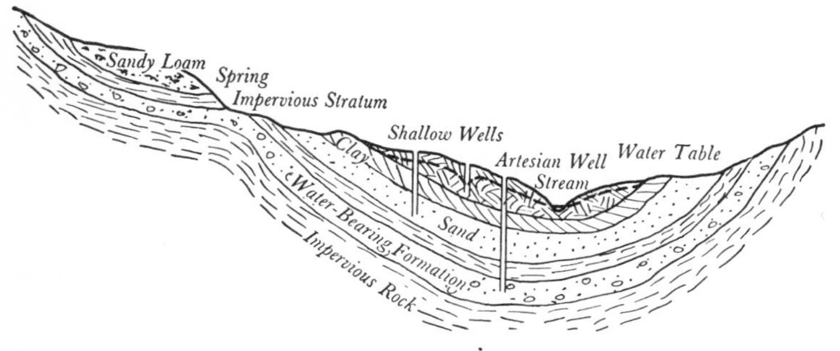

FIG. 6 The origin of springs and wells. (From *Water: Yearbook of the U.S. Department of Agriculture*, 1955.)

water-bearing layer may be sealed in a cuplike basin between two impermeable layers, so that when a hole is drilled in the upper layer the pressure of the water from below will produce what is known as an artesian well. In some places the pressure is such as to produce a natural upwelling in the form of an artesian spring. Where the volume of water carried by the aquifer is large, a pool or lake will form, which may in turn be the source of a full-fledged river.

Part of the world's water supply is drawn from these underground storage chambers, some of which are of enormous extent; but even the largest are by no means inexhaustible. Over the centuries, springs and wells have dried up simply as a result of climatic changes. In the Sahara, for example, prehistoric cultures depended upon a supply of ground water far richer than exists today. Where an aquifer meets the slope of the seashore, excessive withdrawal of water will eventually lower the water table to the point that salt water will begin invading the porous layers. The cities of New York and Los Angeles have both already encountered this predicament; to offset it, ordinances have been passed requiring all water used for cooling and air conditioning to be returned to the aquifer from which it was originally withdrawn.

On sloping ground, water from a spring will rush immediately downhill as a brook or cascade. Where the level of the ground water is high, it will feed into the stream (Figure 7); conversely, an aquifer sloping away from a stream may draw water from it. Because spring water may have traveled for miles before emerging, its temperature is generally more stable—colder in summer and warmer in winter—than that of most ponds, lakes, and streams in its vicinity. A spring usually freezes only at the edge, and buttercups and other flowering plants growing about its borders may already be in bloom while there is still snow on the ground.

Spring Life

In a mountain spring without a basin to prevent water from rushing downhill, the plants and animals are similar to those of any small brook or cascade in the same region. Yet spring pools are a special kind of habitat with their own peculiar natural communities. Not only are they cold, but usually they also contain less free oxygen and more dissolved carbon dioxide than the surface waters around them. In limestone regions, lime will be dissolved in the ground

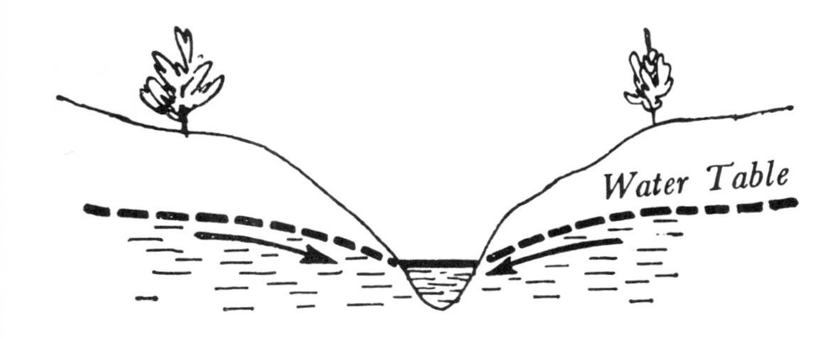

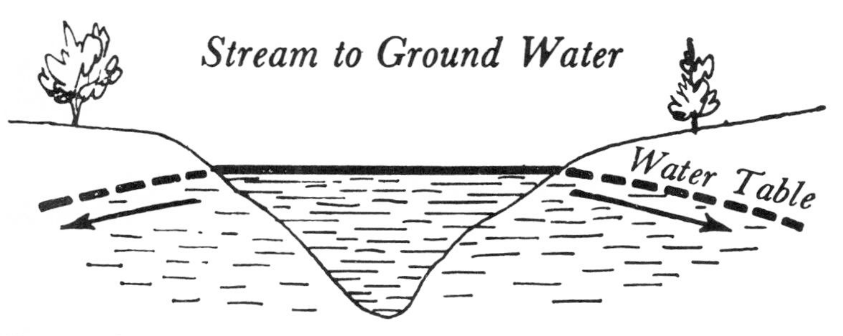

FIG. 7 Ground water seepage in and out of a stream. (From *Water: Yearbook of the U.S. Department of Agriculture*, 1955.)

water in the form of calcium carbonate, and as the excess carbon dioxide escapes into the air at the spring site, the resulting chemical changes in the water will produce lime deposits.*

On a summer day a spring pool in a forest glade or meadow, surrounded by willows and alder bushes, offers an invitation to lie down beside it, drink, and then peer through

* These formations, known as tufa, may build up into mounds around the edge of a spring, and may at times be riddled with the larvae of certain species of the ubiquitous midge family.

the clear surface at the tangle of submerged plants below. These plants and their associated animals have made the same adjustments to cold as those in mountain brooks, without the latter's adaptations to fast water. Covering the stones are delicately colored algae and diatoms, mosses, and such flowering plants as water cress. In limestone regions, however, the larger plants may consist chiefly of stonewort (*Chara*), a large alga with a central stem and whorls of branches that grow upward for a foot or two.

Despite the water's chemical composition, the plant mats of a spring offer protection to many small animals. One type, a greenish-brown shrimplike creature, rarely strays from plant cover. This creature moves by straightening its body and beating with swimming legs attached to the abdominal segments, often rolling over sidewise as it swims —a peculiar locomotion that has earned it the name side-swimmer. Two genera commonly found in springs are *Gammarus* and *Hyalella*, which are distinguished from each other by slight differences in their antennae.

Sideswimmers, or scuds, as they also are called, are active mainly at night, emerging from the vegetation to go on feeding expeditions as dusk comes on (Figure 8). Omnivorous scavengers, they hold sizable pieces of food with their forefeet and they eat without first tearing them into smaller pieces. During the day they may also browse on the film of microscopic plants and animals covering the leaves and stems of the submerged plants.

These arthropods, members of the order Amphipoda, have a high reproductive potential; there have been reports of spring brooks with more than 10,000 individuals per square yard of vegetation. A female lays about eighteen eggs per brood, with as many as fifteen broods in less than half a year, and the number of survivors depends almost entirely upon the limitations of the existing food supply, since amphipods are preyed upon only by an occasional diving beetle, salamander, frog, or turtle, or now and then a wading bird.

Other arthropods conspicuous in springs are the water mites or Hyrachnida, relatives of the spiders. Like the water insects (and also like the whales and porpoises), these are

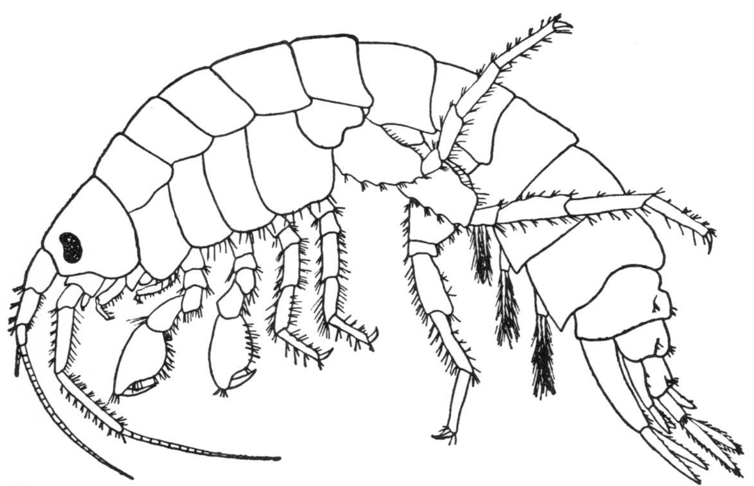

FIG. 8 Scud or sideswimmer (*Gammarus fasciatus*). (From Pennak, 1953.)

former land animals that have returned to an aquatic way of life. Water mites appear as pinhead-sized, brilliantly red- or yellow-and-black orbs gliding below the surface. A microscope is needed to see how they swim—by flailing four pairs of legs covered with microscopic swimming hairs (Figure 9).

The body of a true spider is divided into the trunk, or cephalothorax, and the abdomen; but the body of the water mite, though it belongs to the same zoological class, has lost this division and has evolved into a ventrally flattened sphere. On its underside, where the minute legs are attached, are the mouthparts—a pair of palps and a pair of mandibles, which in some species are formidable stiletto- or saber-like weapons.

Water mites and scuds are especially typical of springs, but they are by no means the only animals found there. Worms, snails, and various insects and their larvae—notably

FIG. 9 Water mite (*Mideopsis*), ventral view. (From Pennak, 1953.)

water beetles and bugs—occur in springs, which they colonize just as they would any suitable slow-flowing portion of a brook or stream.

GROUND WATER AND CAVE LIFE

In spring pools with a strong flow, turbulent places with a slight upwelling show just where the water bubbles out of a subterranean source—the aquifer itself, or from an intervening fissure, duct, or even a cave. Some animals have invaded these dim water-filled haunts and become adjusted to the peculiar conditions there. The scuds, for instance, have colorless relatives that may now and then be inadvertently carried upward into the daylight of the spring itself.

Most typical ground-water and cave species are colorless and many even lack eyes; but over the ages, as an adaptation to perpetual darkness, their chemical and tactile senses have become well developed in compensation for their lack of sight. Cave shrimp have enormous antennae, and the fins and body of the cave fish (*Amblyopsis spelaea*) are equipped with a pincushionlike array of lateral line receptors —a series of special sense organs hidden in jelly-filled canals on the head and along the side of the body, where they are most conspicuous as a dark line extending from the gills to the tail. Organs similar to those that compose this lateral line are also present in some amphibians, serving to detect vibrations and small movements in the water such as would be produced by a swimming or creeping prey. Lateral-line organs are found to some degree in all fishes, but they are especially well developed and profuse in those that inhabit the abyssal waters of the ocean, where there is no light, and in cave-dwellers. The Dutch physiologist Sven Dijkgraaf has described these organs by the paradoxical but accurate phrase "touch sense at a distance."

The life history of the grotto salamander (*Typhlotriton spelaeus*) offers a clue to how certain animals have invaded underground waters. The larva lives in streams outside limestone caves, making use of normally functioning eyes to hunt for aquatic insects. But when it is ready to transform into an adult, it finds the entrance to a cave and takes to living underground, whereupon its eyelids simply grow shut. It is not difficult to imagine how some of the amphibians, whose fossils date back more than 200 million years, might have become permanent cave-dwellers. First there would have been occasional forays underground to feed on an otherwise unused source of food; but since there was not enough there to permit raising numerous young, the latter would still be hatched and reared outside. Finally, along with such mutations as the change in color to white or pink, and the gradual regression of the eyes—developments neither of which would interfere with survival in permanent darkness—there must have been other, more positive genetic changes. While in the cave salamanders the senses of taste and touch and the organs of the lateral line evolved an extraordinary keenness that compensated for the loss of vision, other mutations occurred in their breeding behavior that led to greater care for the eggs and young than is typical of surface-dwelling amphibians. Cave salamanders probably breed the year round since there are no seasons underground. New species of cave-dwellers are now and then discovered by accident in the depths of wells, several hundred feet below the surface; but the realm of underground darkness is still one of the least explored habitats on earth.

Life Around the Spring

Springs and small brooks which offer cool water and shade, the protection of stones, moss-covered banks, heavy undergrowth, and the absence of predatory fishes, are the favored haunts of salamanders. Many species slip in and out of the water with ease, whereas others never leave it; but they all must have enough moisture around them to prevent their skins from drying out. These silent amphibians are less familiar to most people than the often vociferous frogs and toads; they are also more secretive, either by disposition or as a result of their need for constant moisture.

Any salamander seen in or near a spring in North America is apt to belong to one of the lungless genera.

These amphibians are usually small, ranging in length from an inch and a half to six or seven inches, but are often strikingly colored. The red salamander (*Pseudotriton ruber*), for example, is orange-red with iridescent black spots on its back, and has yellow eyes. It lives near springs or in other moist places, and hunts for its diet of insects and worms mainly at dusk, as do most salamanders—another reason why they are so rarely seen.

Another of the lungless species is the spring or purple salamander (*Gyrinophilus porphyriticus*), whose scientific name indicates both its vivid color and its preference for cold mountain springs, brooks, or seepage areas. Some species of salamanders have a very restricted distribution: another spring salamander (also of the genus *Gyrinophilus*) occurs only in the southern part of the Blue Ridge Mountains, and still another has been found only in the swales on Grandfather Mountain in North Carolina.

Many salamanders, the cave-dwelling species among them, lay their eggs in protected places under a stone or a log, where they are guarded by the female. Some species even practice a form of internal fertilization; the male deposits the sperm in a capsule, the spermatophore, which he induces the female to insert into her vent, where fertilization then takes place. Relatively few eggs are produced, compared to the numbers laid by some fishes or by those frogs—the majority of species—that fertilize their eggs externally. This relatively complex breeding behavior is coordinated with postures and movements peculiar to the species; in one instance the male literally rubs noses with the female, thus emptying a gland on his chin whose contents stimulate the female to search for the spermatophore.

Few birds and mammals entirely restrict their habitats to the banks of streams, and none is found exclusively around springs. Nevertheless the moisture and the dense plant cover which ensure shelter and an abundant food supply lead to frequent visits by mice and voles, and in some places by raccoons; even an occasional fox may be attracted. If the spring flows into a small ravine, the dense underbrush there may be the site of a whippoorwill's nest—a structure so well concealed that it is usually found by accident rather than by following the direction of the unseen bird's call.

A spring at the edge of the forest or out in the open will often be surrounded by a small marsh and a few alders and willows. These will attract certain marsh-dwelling birds; small brown swamp sparrows with their sweet, bell-like song will feed on the seeds of sedges, and there may be a small colony of the larger, more conspicuous redwinged blackbirds (*Agelaius phoeniceus*). The male redwings arrive from their wintering places in March or April, depending on the latitude. They are strikingly colored birds, with their sleek black plumage, which has a greenish gloss, set off by upper wing coverts that form a bright red patch with a band of yellow underneath.

After searching for a suitable territory in a marsh or near a spring, the male redwing will perch on a reed or an alder branch, whistling and calling stridently—his way of warning all other males to keep out of his territory and at the same time advertising himself to the females, which follow the males northward at an interval of about ten days. A territorial male may father several broods, hatched from pale blue eggs with scribblelike marks of brown scattered over them, in a nest woven of grasses and sedges. So long as the meadow is not drained and the spring remains uncapped, the birds raised in a particular marsh are likely to return there year after year. The mock-fights, the posturing at the borders of the territory, and the modulations of the males' warning call during the breeding season are not only fascinating but easy to observe, for redwings are not shy; even their nests are not hard to find.

Bogs

In the mountains and the cooler regions of the globe bogs contribute to the flow of many streams. They differ from ordinary ponds in having acid waters with a very low mineral content and a high content of brown humic materials, the product of an incomplete decomposition of plant remains. The invertebrate animals and especially the plants of bogs are very distinctive. Coming upon a bog in a spruce forest, one passes through a circle of tamarack and white cedar, mixed with a dwindling number of spruce trees which become increasingly small and stunted. Yet the age of these dwarf trees, as revealed by a count of their annual rings, may be a hundred years, even when their stems are only as thick as a man's thumb.

Soon the trees disappear altogether, and the clearing in the forest leads to a lens-shaped, slightly elevated circle of peatmoss (*Sphagnum*), surrounded by dwarf bilberry shrubs, cranberry bushes, and–in the northernmost states and Canada–by Labrador tea with its white, pommel-like, fragrantly scented flower clusters. The cover of peatmoss may be many feet thick; as its lower layers become compacted by the growth of new plants and the air is totally excluded, it slowly changes into peat, which is a first stage in the formation of coal.

Between the hillocks of peatmoss lie small bog pools. In the boreal forest and in the tundra, where they abound, such pools are the summer breeding grounds of mosquitoes and other biting flies that make life miserable for man and beast–so much so that during the summer the caribou seek the high ridges, where the wind drives the insects away. But relatively few aquatic insects and crustaceans have adapted themselves to the extremely soft, acid waters, and the small number of typical bog invertebrates is an indication of the biological severity of the environment.

Around the edge of the circle of peatmoss and on its hillocks are sedges, interspersed with those botanical curiosities, the insect-eating plants—the sundews with their glistening rosettes of leaves, the tubular clusters of pitcher plants, or the peculiar hinged leaves of a Venus' flytrap. Insect-eating plants are typical of bogs and other soils deficient in nitrogen, since they can obtain a supplement of this element by trapping unsuspecting flies, ants, or other insects. The pitcher plant has vase-shaped leaves; these are lined with nectar-producing glands to attract spiders and insects. Downward-pointing hairs on the leaves prevent escape, and each pitcher has a miniature pool of water at the bottom where the unwary victims drown, subsequently to be digested by the joint action of the plant's own enzymes and of bacteria which live in the water.

A close study of pitcher plants has revealed the remarkable fact that some insects—one species of mosquito and several midges—rear their larvae in the water of the very traps that are deathly to all other flying and crawling forms of life. These peculiar commensals do not seem to be affected by the enzymes of the plant; in fact they feed on the partially digested remains of animals that have drowned in the pitchers.

Other carnivorous bog plants catch their prey in still other ways. The leaves of the sundew are covered with stout hairs, each tipped by a sticky globule, again containing tissue-dissolving enzymes. When an insect alights it is caught by the glue on one or two hairs; other adjacent hairs bend over, and the process of digestion begins. The leaves of the Venus' flytrap are even more acrobatic in capturing the prey. The circular leaf blade is hinged along the middle and bordered with a row of stiff, hairlike teeth; in addition it bears touch-sensitive hairs and red-pigmented glands that produce enzymes along with a sugary secretion. As the victim alights, triggering one of the hairs, the two halves of the leaf close, the marginal teeth crossing to prevent the insect from crawling out. During the next few hours the blades close tight and the fly is digested; then after a few days the leaf opens again, ready to trap another victim. Carnivorous plants, incidentally, can live without animal food, but in the bog, where dissolved nitrates are scarce, their insect harvest allows them to grow faster and to mature earlier than they would if no additional nitrogen were available.

Bogs are typical of poorly drained, infertile regions. They occur in small hollows and depressions among the high mountains, and are especially numerous throughout the Canadian Shield—an area covering much of Canada and extending into the northeastern United States, where the ancient bedrock lies close to the surface. A bog will also be found wherever a small northern fresh-water lake has become overgrown with plants and choked with their remains. This is an inevitable development: sooner or later, every such lake becomes a bog.

Lakes

Permanent though they appear, lakes are in fact transitory features of the landscape. From the moment they are formed they begin to undergo change; they are gradually filled in, and finally they disappear, as a result of the same processes that are involved in the formation of streams. Like streams, lakes are fed by precipitation, either directly in the form of rain or snow, or indirectly from underground accumulations or the melting of glaciers. They form the headwaters of many streams—Lake Itasca in Minnesota, for example, gives rise to the Mississippi—and are in turn fed by streams, which deposit sand, silt, and other debris accumulated along their courses. The unloading of these sediments on the bed of a lake, and along its shores, leads eventually to its filling in and to its final disappearance. The process is hastened where an already well-defined stream flows into a lake, depositing its load of sediments, and then emerges as a larger and more transparent river. Such a lake is essentially no more than a temporary widening of the river bed.

Lakes as a rule, in fact, consist of flowing waters on their way to the sea, although some notable exceptions occur in arid regions. The Great Salt Lake is an example; it is fed by streams that rise in the surrounding mountains, but at some time in the comparatively recent past the water level fell drastically as a result of evaporation, and the lake no longer has an outlet. Many smaller but similar lakes in desert regions actually dry up during a part of every year, or contain water only after a rain. The absence of any outflowing stream leads to the depositing of mineral salts which would otherwise have remained in solution, to be carried into the sea; thus such lakes are salty or alkaline, and contain little plant or animal life.

All lakes, whether salt or fresh, consist fundamentally of an accumulation of water in a basin. The basin itself may have been produced in any of a variety of ways. Not a few lakes are man-made, the result of the damming of a stream so as to create a basin. The blocking of a valley by a landslide, by sediments brought in by a tributary, or by the piling up of rocky debris into a moraine at the foot of a valley glacier, may produce a lake in exactly the same way. Oxbow lakes are formed when the meanders of a slow-moving stream are short-circuited and then cut off entirely. Still other lakes occupy basins produced by earthquakes or as the aftermath of a volcanic eruption: Crater Lake in Oregon is a noted example of the latter.

But lake basins are most commonly the work of glaciers. As the mountains of ice advanced, the scouring action of their massive load of rocky debris deepened valleys previously carved by rivers, and meltwater accumulating at the edge of the continental glaciers was held in by moraines or spilled over into preglacial valleys. Such legacies of the ice age include Lake Geneva and Lake Constance in Europe, the New York Finger Lakes, and—most spectacular of all—the North American Great Lakes. These inland seas are linked in a single continuous waterway, each link at a somewhat lower level than the preceding, and flowing eastward to empty into the St. Lawrence. Because of their vast size, hundreds of years are required for a given mass of water to pass through any of the Great Lakes. Nevertheless, even they are continually subject both to the processes of erosion and deposition that will eventually bring an end to their existence, and to the annual cycle of changes typical of smaller lakes.

The Yearly Cycle of a Lake

In a stream the temperature is relatively uniform from the top to the bottom; but the water in a lake is stratified in layers of different density and temperature. In winter, because fresh water is densest and heaviest not at freezing but at about 40° F., the coldest water will be that directly under the ice, while the slightly warmer water will sink to the bottom. For this reason lakes cannot freeze solid, and the animals in them thus have a place to overwinter. Once a thin sheet of ice has formed, it serves to insulate the water; and it thickens so slowly that even lakes far in the Canadian Arctic rarely have an ice cover of more than six or seven feet. The water of a frozen lake cannot be mixed by the wind; thus the water masses at the top and the bottom remain separate. In fertile, shallow lakes or ponds with large animal communities, this may mean that all the dissolved oxygen will be used up; and if that occurs, a winterkill of fishes and other animals will be the result.

In spring, after the ice has thawed, the sun begins to warm

the surface water and the wind to stir and mix the water layers. In this way the nutrients from the bottom are carried to the surface, where algae are soon flourishing and the yearly cycle of growth and production begins once more. The sun's heat spreads but slowly through water, so that only the top layers warm up at all rapidly; the temperature of those near the bottom never rises much above 39° F. At the same time the wind is helping to distribute the warmed water to a deeper level than would otherwise be possible, and the water is also continually becoming less dense as rapidly as it warms; as a result, by early summer there is a sharp division between the upper and lower waters of a lake. The deeper, colder layer is sealed off from the top by a zone of rapid thermal transition, called the thermocline. Oxygen cannot diffuse through it; thus, especially in fertile lakes, the bacteria in the mud, along with the worms, the snails, and all other bottom animals, may face oxygen depletion again, this time in midsummer.

In the fall, the cooler air lowers the temperature of the surface water, again increasing its density until it approaches that of the bottom layer. Usually by November the entire water mass is of equal density and the wind produces a "fall overturn," as hydrobiologists call the event that allows the bottom regions to become re-saturated with oxygen. Shortly thereafter the surface water cools still further, and the lake freezes over once more.

This cycle, the result of the peculiar physical properties of water, is typical of lakes in the Northern Hemisphere, and in its turn influences the distribution of life to be found there. In some lakes nothing would survive if water were densest at 32°, rather than at 39.2° F., since then the lake could turn into a solid block of ice. Obviously a deep mountain lake, nourished by streams of low fertility, will have fewer animals in it than a shallower lowland lake that receives water from the rich soils around it; and in the former the midsummer and midwinter reduction in oxygen of the bottom water will accordingly be less pronounced. In fact, lakes have been classified on this basis as oligotrophic (from the Greek words *oligos*—"little" or "few"—and *trophein*—"to grow"), and eutrophic (using the Greek prefix *eu*, for "much" or "good").

Perch and bass, among many other fishes, seek their food on the bottom of eutrophic lakes; and during the winter, unless the oxygen vanishes completely from its deeper waters, they will remain there, since water of a temperature just above freezing is too cold for the comfort of either perch or bass. Such fishes as the cisco and the wall-eyed pike prefer cool water in the summer but also require a large supply of oxygen; they will therefore go down into the thermocline to seek the cooler water just as far as the dwindling oxygen supply will allow. In hot years the thermocline can become a very narrow zone, and the fish may be in considerable distress; in some summers they may even suffocate there, and their bodies will then float up and litter the beaches. Fishermen obviously might do well to locate the thermocline and weight their lines accordingly. Along the 49th parallel in America the thermocline in an average lake begins at between twenty and thirty feet.

Streams flowing into a lake are often cooler than the lake's surface, so that the inflowing water will sink immediately. A heavy silt load may also change the over-all density of the inflow, and the incoming river will be traceable as a veritable underwater waterfall; it may then carve a subaqueous channel, as it does at the mouth of the upper Rhine in Lake Constance and of the Rhone in Lake Geneva. However, a stream or river coming out of a lake will bring water from the surface and for some distance will reflect the yearly cycle of lake surface temperatures, although downstream its temperature will once again become uniform.

Lake Plankton

Attached algae form the base of the food chain in a stream, and many animals that feed on them also are adapted to remain attached to the substrate. In lakes and ponds, on the other hand, as well as in the ocean, both algae and minute animals can take advantage of the flotation power of the water; here they have no need for holdfast devices, except in the surf zone near the shore. The plant base of lake life therefore consists predominantly of floating algae, or phytoplankton. The small animals that feed on these minute plants and that in turn provide food for many larger animals are known collectively as zooplankton. The word *plankton* is Greek for "that which is made to wander or drift"; *phyton* and *zoon*, of course, respectively mean plant and animal. The many algae and invertebrate animals that occur in the plankton constitute a weird miniature world of their own.

Arthropod crustaceans, small relatives of the shrimp, predominate in animal plankton. Fishes forage for them in the open water of a lake or the sea; krill, the food of whales, is likewise composed of such plankton, as is the food of herring and sardines; and in lakes whitefish and young trout, perch and young bass all gorge themselves on minute freshwater crustaceans.

For collecting plankton a biologist will use a series of conical nets, made of bolting cloth with graduated mesh sizes; but there is a simpler method of sampling the plankton of a lake. A nylon stocking, fastened around the top to an embroidery hoop and held submerged while one is slowly rowing, will let the water pass and retain the larger plankters (as plankton organisms are known collectively). If after no more than ten minutes the foot of the stocking is everted into a glass, the pullulating movements of many plankters will show up against the light.

Under a microscope most of the animals will turn out to be shrimplike—segmented and possessing antennae, a chitinous carapace, jointed legs with bristles on them, and a forked tail, ending in several long hairs. Such animals are copepods (Figure 10), members of a crustacean order typi-

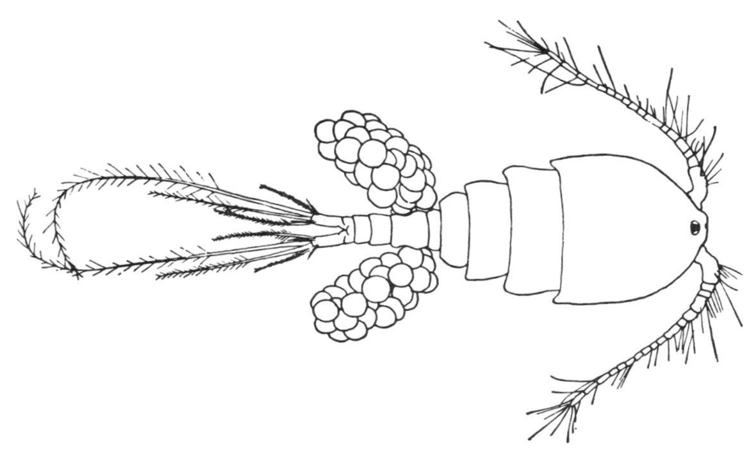

FIG. 10 Typical copepod (*Macrocyclops ater*); a female with egg clusters is shown. (From Pennak, 1953.)

cal of lake zooplankton. A sample in early summer will almost certainly contain females with grapelike clusters of orange eggs attached to the abdomen. The animals are translucent, and oil globules under the exoskeleton will be visible, as is the bright orange eye spot on top of the head. The orange tints are due to carotenoids, chemical compounds similar to Vitamin A, and they in turn are responsible for the pink flesh of salmon and of those trout for which copepods are directly or indirectly a source of food.

Copepods are difficult to watch under the microscope because of their jerky movements. In one moment they may be clearly seen as their antennules sweep algae and other minute foods into their mouths; in the next, with a sudden oar-stroke of the first pair of antennae they have vanished out of the field. Although they are not, in fact, propelled by their antennae but rather by a rapid backward beat of the legs, the antennae because of their size must be folded quickly, just before the stroke, so as not to impede the animal's forward movement. Immediately after the stroke the antennae are spread again and act in the manner of a parachute, retarding the copepod's natural tendency to sink. Among the plankters will be many squat, rounded creatures somewhat reminiscent of the spring-dwelling water mites; these are larvae of copepods, the so-called nauplii. Since a

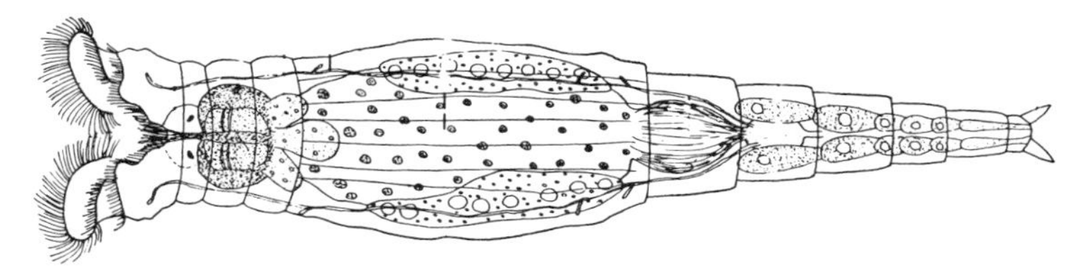

FIG. 11 Rotifer. Note "wheels" on ciliary crown. (From Pennak, 1953.)

copepod goes through several nauplius stages before maturing, those latter are usually more numerous than the adults.

Yet another group of zooplankters likely to be represented in the haul with the stocking are the rotifers. Smaller than the copepods, they are perhaps the most typical of all fresh-water plankton. Whereas those of almost any other group will have several, and often indeed many, close relatives in the sea, rotifers have few. The name *rotifer*, Latin for "wheel-bearer," refers to a crown of fine hairs or cilia on the head of some species (Figure 11); these beat in such a fashion as to suggest a miniature pair of revolving wheels. In addition to the ciliary crown, rotifers have a prominent chewing apparatus—the mastax—composed of muscles and finely chiseled chitinous structures for grinding, shearing, or tearing, which vary in design according to the food of the species.

Most rotifiers in any plankton sample will be females; males are rarely seen, since they are both minute and short-lived. The male rotifer, having no mouth, no mastax, and no digestive organs, obviously does not feed; in fact it is nothing but a sperm sac with a penis, surrounded by a cuticle, and with a tuft of cilia in front to enable it to reach a female. Male rotifers hatch from eggs of a special type which are laid by certain females, likewise of a special type, only at certain times of the year, for example when there is a scarcity of food or a drop in temperature.

The Aging of Lakes

Lakes vanish from the landscape not only through absorbing the silt loads deposited by streams and rivers, but also as a result of biological processes. The chitinous and siliceous shells of millions of plankton organisms drop to the bottom and are added to the sediments of sand, clay, or silt. Even though these deposits of plant and animal remains may reduce the depth in the center of a lake by no more than a minute fraction of an inch a year, the life of a lake is to be reckoned in thousands or tens of thousands of years, as opposed to the millions in that of a river. Lakes become more fertile as they become shallower; rooted aquatic plants emerge, whose effect is to slow down wave action, to trap sediments, and to act as a kind of green manure for the marsh and wetland plants that will eventually replace them.

Organic nutrients, as well as such compounds as phosphates and nitrates, are carried down from the watershed, and in many lakes—especially those that are not furrow-shaped but have various arms, bays, and inlets—only a fraction of the yearly mineral additions are carried out of the lake again by the streams emerging from it. In a lake, as compared to a river, the volume of water is large in proportion to the bottom area of its basin; this mass of water, with its annual cycle of turnover and stagnation, retards the rise in over-all fertility and productivity. Nevertheless, as the lake becomes shallower and warmer, its plankton, plants, bottom animals, and fishes become more varied and numerous. Differences between youthful mountain lakes and older lowland bodies of water can be expressed in terms of fish. A deep, cold lake will produce between 40 and 60 pounds of fish—mostly consisting of trout and whitefish—per surface acre per year, whereas in the same length of time a eutrophic lake may bring forth up to 400 pounds of fish per acre; however, these will be mostly carp, bullheads, and perch, with some bluegills but only a few pike and bass.

Once its watersheds have been given over to agriculture, there comes a point when the fertility of a lake increases rapidly, indicating without a doubt that its once cool, blue waters are soon to be replaced by a shallow marsh traversed by a slow stream. This is a natural process, over which we have no control, although it may be retarded if the various influences at work are taken into account. In some ways the aging of a stream resembles that of a lake. But a stream will vanish completely only when its source disappears; and whereas the aging of a lake is caused largely by biological forces within it, the processes by which a stream passes from youth through maturity and old age are mainly geological. Those processes will be described in the next chapter.

3

Streams

A STREAM IS YOUTHFUL, GEOLOGICALLY SPEAKING, WHEN IT flows through a V-shaped gorge or ravine, with frequent rapids, cascades, and waterfalls. As the incline becomes less steep and the current correspondingly less rapid, the channel tends to widen into the U-shaped valley of a stream nearing maturity. As the increasing amounts of sand and silt laid down by the current form a flood plain with meanders and oxbows—horseshoe bends that fold back on themselves (Figure 12), eventually giving rise to oxbow lakes—the stream will be described as mature. An exceedingly wide flood plain with natural levees, and with many places where the waters resemble those of a eutrophic lake, typifies a stream in old age.

Although a stream in old age is most commonly a large river, the entire sequence—or at any rate a part of it—may recur more than once along the course of even a relatively

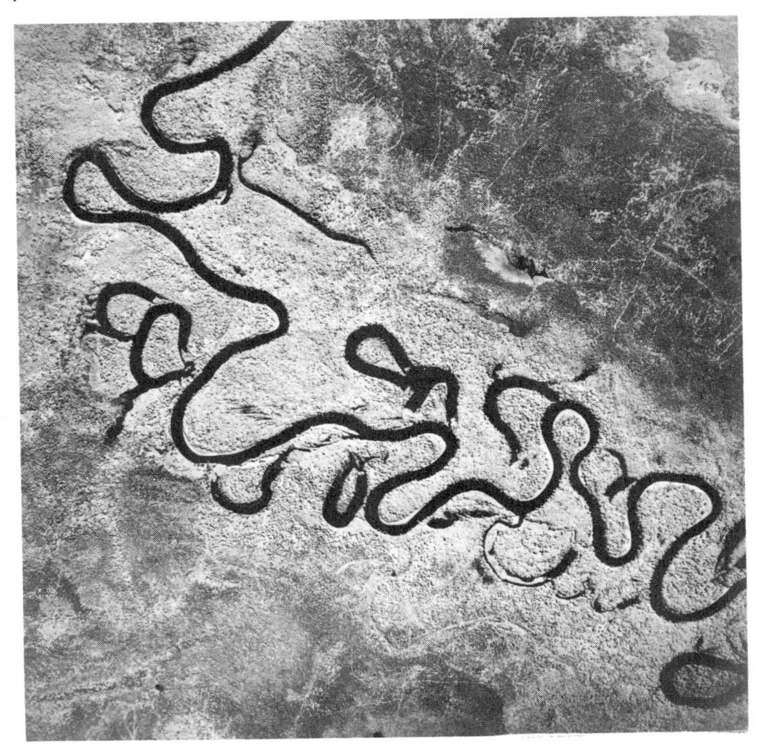

Fig. 12 Aerial photograph of meanders and oxbows. Photo from U.S. Department of Agriculture.

small stream. The form taken by any watercourse at a particular point is determined not by the absolute distance from its source but by the relative steepness of the incline, the nature of the soil or rock over which it flows, and the degree of fluctuation (rather than the absolute volume) of the water it carries. In general, it is true, the gradient and the speed of smaller streams tend to be more extreme than those of rivers; and these two variables to some extent also influence the temperature of the water, so that in summer the tributaries are usually colder than the main stream.

A river, again, is ordinarily large and deep enough to be navigable, whereas a stream may carry a canoe or a sampan, and a brook or creek will not admit any kind of craft. Otherwise, no real distinction between a brook and a stream, or between a stream and a river, can easily be made. All three produce traces that are essentially alike. Typically, a brook that has its rise at a glacier's edge will form a braided channel, along a bed through which the water flows in a tangle of converging and diverging traces (Figure 13). On the other hand, even a glacial stream may sometimes form miniature meanders and oxbows; and the lower reaches of a great river such as the Amazon, with its shifting sand-banks and alluvial islands, may follow a braided pattern. Precisely the same pattern may be observed in the sediment-loaded rills that form along a roadside after a heavy rain. It will occur wherever there are sudden changes in the amount of flowing water, together with loose soil and a moderately steep incline—just as cascades or a waterfall will form wherever there are sills of resistant rock, and a flood plain with meanders wherever the slope becomes more gradual.

The Color of Flowing Water

Along with its form, the color of a stream may change many times as it flows from a meadow into a forest, from an open valley into a narrow gorge, or from a sandy bottom to one of stones, mud, or silt. Pure water is itself almost colorless; dissolved and suspended materials are what impart color to it. Moorland tarns and brooks are brown owing to humic acids dissolved in them; limestone springs and streams contain minerals that give their waters a slightly bluish tint. Pond and lake waters are often green or yellow because of abundant floating algae, whose pigments reflect green or yellow while they absorb the other colors of the spectrum.

The same selective absorption of certain colors comes

Fig. 13 Braided stream pattern in Alaska. Photo courtesy Professor D. Baxter.

into play in clear water that is more than a foot or two deep. Even the water in a white enamel bathtub will have a faint blue-green tint because some of the violet, blue, and green components of white light pass through the water, while the orange and red wave-lengths are absorbed. The deeper the layer through which the light passes, the stronger this effect becomes; on an open lake or on the ocean, it is further enhanced by the surface reflection of the blue sky above. The purer the water the bluer it appears, as may be observed in lakes whose tributaries have flowed only over granite rock or over forested soils of low fertility, and thus do not carry suspended materials.

Streams and rivers, though, are often muddy and brown. Most important among the suspended particles to which their color is due are the soil colloids. These are so small that they may take over fifty years to sink one foot in completely still water. Clay particles, which will likewise impart color to streams and rivers, are also very small (1/1000 of a millimeter in diameter), and settle slowly—about one foot per year in still water—thus delaying the clearing of muddy rivers.

The colors of a stream also reflect the shades and hues of its bottom; the color of the sky is imparted to the water as is the green canopy of the trees that border the stream, or the white, grey, or brown of rocks along its banks. The reflected greens may be anything from the green-gold tint of new aspen leaves to the dark, saturated hue of black spruce or hemlock, or the gradations of blue-green peculiar to any of various pines; all these impart their own hue as they are reflected in the moving mirror of the stream.

Most of the bottom colors that tinge the water are likewise due to plant pigments. Various algae and mosses, and many submerged leafy plants, themselves often becoming encrusted with minute vegetation, may be brown, yellow, or even black. Underwater plant beds can make the stream appear somber and mysterious; the brown bark of submerged logs can have the same effect. Streams with sandy bottoms are often golden yellow or silvery white, and the interplay of sunlight with the sand on the ridges created by the flow produces a kaleidoscopic pattern of light and shade.

Plants and Animals as Indicators of Stream Flow

The speed of flow determines whether the bottom of the stream will be composed of rubble, pebbles, sand, or silt; and the nature of this substrate largely governs the nature of the vegetation that will grow there. Larger aquatic plants, for instance, can hardly occur among pebbles, but will readily grow in silt. In the same way, the kinds and abundance of the animals inhabiting a particular section of the stream will reflect the nature of the plant substrate—but also, often more importantly, the speed of the water. This is especially true when the stream flow becomes torrential and holdfast organs assume progressively greater importance. Variants of the sucking discs of the net-winged midges, now familiar from the description of their life habits in waterfalls, occur in rapid-stream dwellers throughout the world. Especially in the tropics, where ice and snow do not arrest the yearly life cycle of plants and animals, there have evolved an array of sucking discs and holdfast devices among a wide variety of animals.

In the cascades of Borneo and Malaya waterfall-inhabiting crickets, snails, tadpoles, frogs, and fishes are to be found. In some of the fishes, the processes of evolution have turned fins and entire ventral surfaces into sucking discs; others hang on suspended by their fleshy lips. But as often happens, specialized adaptation creates problems of its own. When a fish uses the mouth as a holdfast, not only feeding but especially breathing becomes difficult, since fishes normally inhale water through the mouth, pass it over the gills, extract the oxygen, and then exhale it through the gill slits. The armored catfishes of the Andes, to take one instance, have solved the problem by means of small grooves on the lips, through which they obtain water for respiration without having to detach themselves from the rocks while they scrape loose the algae and diatoms that make up their food. A fish of the mountain waters in northern Thailand has its gill opening divided into two channels, the upper one serving to lead the water into the gill chamber, the lower one to expel it. Thus equipped the fish can devote itself simultaneously to both feeding and holding on.

A good footing is still important, even in less rapid streams: whether they are found in Colorado, in Switzerland, in Laos, or in Brazil, their plant and animal communities are basically much alike (Figure 14). Indeed, identical species may be found under the same conditions in widely separated localities. This is notably true of algae: a comparison of the species found in the Rhine, the Volga, the Thames, the Yangtze, and the Paraguay rivers showed that between 20 and 30 per cent of the total number of species found in any one river were also to be found in each of the others, and the rest of the species showed striking similarities.

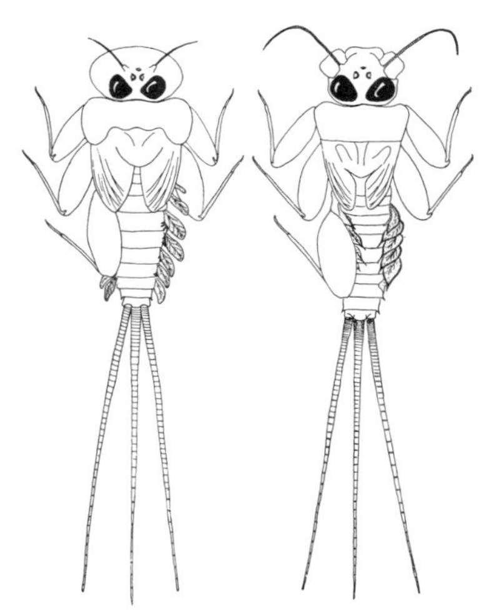

FIG. 14 Two mayfly nymphs—*left*, from a mountain stream in Europe; *right*, from a similar stream in the Andes—show the ubiquitous influence of stream conditions on the shape and structure of animals. (From Illies, Vol. XIV, *Proceedings of the International Association of Theoretical and Applied Limnology*, 1961.)

The precise adaptation of plant life to the speed of the current may be seen in the moss *Fontinalis*, which lends its green color to the slower sections of many a stream. The plant consists of stems that float out from the sand or small gravel in which it is anchored, with small, closely set leaves that offer a minimum of resistance to the movement of the water. The plants themselves become thinner or bushier in proportion to the speed of the current, and the stems' resistance to tearing is likewise proportionate to water speed. The tensile strength of stems can be measured by attaching a graduated series of weights to them until they break. A stem of *Fontinalis* growing in a rapid stream and measuring one millimeter in diameter tore only after being subjected to a weight of more than a pound; a slow-stream form having the same diameter broke when subjected to a weight of just over half a pound. An examination under the microscope showed that the greater tensile strength of the first was due to a thicker outer cell layer—a characteristic no doubt evolved in response to the relatively greater force of the current.

Some leafy flowering plants that re-invaded the water long after they had first conquered the land are abundant in streams. Most of these cannot tolerate torrential conditions; but at the not inconsiderable flow of about two feet per second, stands of water crowfoot (*Ranunculus aquaticus*) and of some narrow-leaved pondweeds (genus *Potamogeton*) can become established. Water cress, though often called an underwater plant in the United States (where, incidentally, it is not a native but a naturalized settler from Europe), is restricted to shallow water with a slow rate of flow, and often emerges in tangled masses, filling springs and cold spring brooks.

The submerged leaves of both the water crowfoot and the pondweed are thin and dissected into many narrow thread- or ribbonlike lobes or leaflets so as to offer minimal resistance to the movement of water. However, the leaves of the water crowfoot that emerge above the water are shaped like those of its relatives, the less aquatic buttercups.

Although species like the water crowfoot do produce flowers, stream plants carry on reproduction mainly by vegetative means. On land, new areas are colonized mainly by seedlings, the issue of sexual reproduction; but in moving water, seeds often cannot take hold, and the spread of plants proceeds largely by means of runners or shoots from the rootstocks. Since the plants thus produced are genetically the same as their parents, variations such as occur as a result of cross-fertilization are less likely to take place than on land. The element of chance, rather than of competition, is largely responsible for the precise composition of any stand of submerged plants. Furthermore, changes in the water level and in the speed of the current lead to shifts in the composition of the stream bottom itself that are more rapid and extreme than any comparable change on land. Thus the composition of any community of plants in a stream changes frequently, drastically, and in a haphazard fashion, from year to year and even from month to month.

The dense cushions of algae and mosses, the stems and leaves of water plants, the underside of loose stones, and the spaces around the pebbles, where the speed of the flow is reduced, provide living spaces for most of the animals of the stream. Many of these—perhaps the greatest number—are microscopic ciliated protozoa, rotifers, and other minute invertebrates. Like the small, rock-encrusting algae of the glacial streams described in the previous chapter, they are able to take advantage of surface tension and viscosity because of their minute size, whereas larger animals, including the many insect larvae, make use of either of the shelter provided by stones and plants, or of special adaptations of their own to life in flowing waters.

Just how important underwater vegetation is to aquatic animals appears from a comparative study made of a British stream. A square yard with a bottom consisting of loose stones had been colonized by something over 3,000 animals, mostly insect larvae; an equal area, consisting of stones with a cover of algae and moss, had ten times that number; in a stand of pondweed over a bottom of silt mixed with pebbles

—where stems and branches reaching to the surface provided many additional levels for attachment—the number of animals was six times that found in the algae substrate.

Stream Insects

The riffles where the water is shallow and turbulent, foaming into white crests over the stones, might not appear to be the most habitable area in the stream. Yet many a trout, dazzled by an angler's lure, has been caught in just such a place. And this is no accident. Underneath the algae- or moss-covered stones and rocky overhangs, a close inspection—all the better if it is conducted with a hand lens—will show at least some of the organisms that live there and that are the food of trout (Figure 15).

Most of these are insects. A majority of this abundant, diverse, and successful class of animals are terrestrial; but many have aquatic larvae, and some spend their entire lives in or on the water. Aquatic or semiaquatic insects are much more prevalent in or near fresh-water streams, ponds, and the shores of lakes than they are in ocean waters. The habits evolved by these insects for food-gathering and for ensuring the successful development of their young are exceptionally diverse. In size they range from nearly microscopic to a length of two inches. Besides being the chief food of many stream fishes, their larvae show a variety of adaptation to existence in moving water unequaled by any other class of animals.

Among the species common in a trout stream are stonefly larvae (Plecoptera) similar to those that occur in the high mountain stream. They are brown or black, patterned with yellow, and are to be found edging their flattened bodies into cracks and holding on to the stones with their strong claws. On the underside of the same stones, the cases of caddisfly larvae (Trichoptera) will often be numerous—

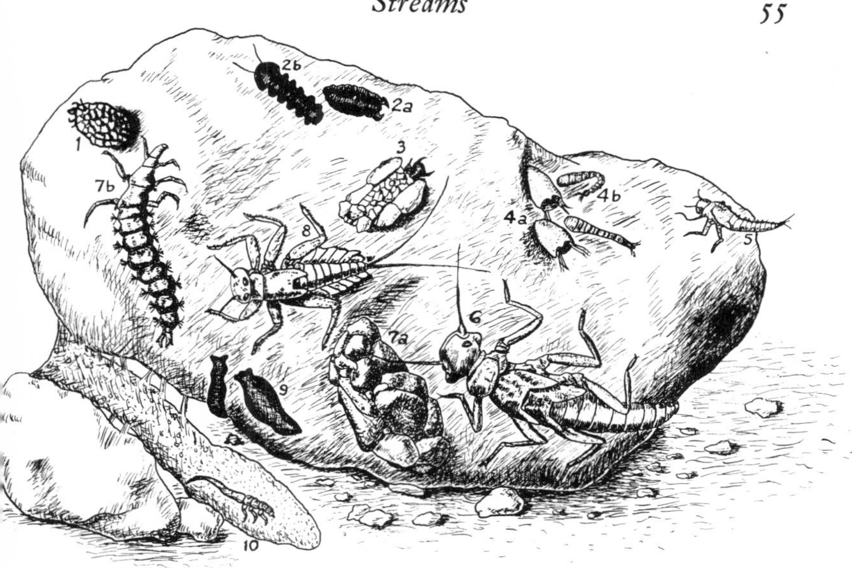

FIG. 15 Ten typical stream animals on and under a stone. *1.* Small caddisfly (*Synagapetus*). *2.* (a and b) Fly larva and pupa (*Liponeura*). *3.* Larval case of the caddisfly (*Goera*). *4.* Blackfly larvae and pupae (*Simulium*). *5.* Mayfly nymph (*Baetis*). *6.* Stonefly nymph (*Perlodes*). 7. (a and b) Case and foraging larva of the caddisfly (*Rhyacophila*). *8.* Mayfly nymph (*Epeorus*). *9.* Planarians. *10.* Caddisfly larva (*Philopotamus*) in its catching net. (After Ruttner, *Fundamentals of Limnology*, 1962.)

small cylinders of regularly arranged sand grains or pebbles, with the chitinous head of the larva or naiad just visible at one end. The term *naiad*, applied to the immature stages of certain aquatic insects, is a borrowing from classical mythology, in which naiads were water nymphs fabled to reside in springs or streams. Upon being removed from the water, small tube-dwellers of this sort will frequently emerge, revealing the soft and delicate hind section, protected by the case; it may be colored green or tan, but is often creamy white (Figure 16).

The case of the caddisfly larva may be fashioned from

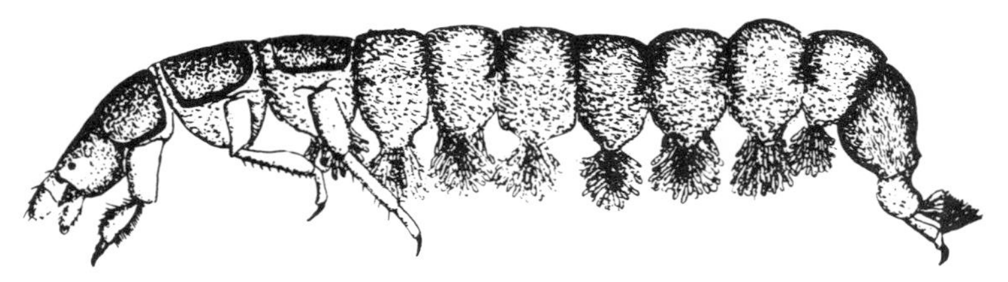

FIG. 16 Caddisfly larva (*Hydropsyche*) out of its shell, showing claws on tail, abdominal gills, and protective chitinous plates on thorax, which often protrude from the case. (From Wesenburg-Lund, 1943.)

any of various materials around a scaffolding composed of a sticky silklike substance extruded from glands near the mouth; each species can be recognized by its case. *Helicopsyche*, for instance, builds its case of sand grains wound into a spiral, like the shell of a snail. *Goera*, an inhabitant of rapid streams, attaches several larger pebbles, symmetrically arranged on either side of its tube, as ballast (Figure 17).

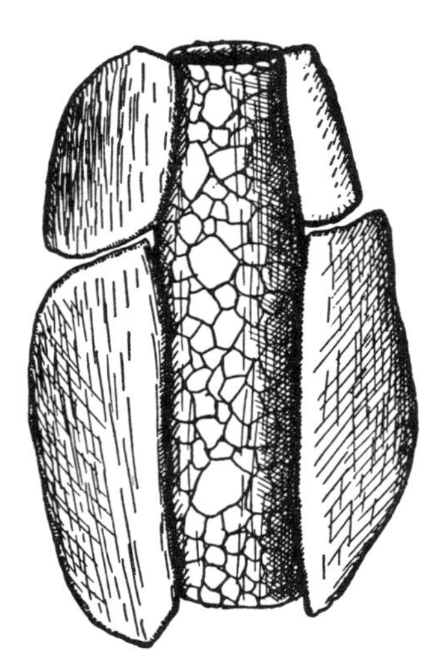

FIG. 17 Case of the caddisfly (*Goera calcarata*) with symmetrically placed ballast stones. (From Pennak, 1953.)

Members of the widespread genus *Limnephilus* build cases from sand, twigs, or leaves, in accordance with the speed of flow and the available materials in their respective habitats. Some caddisfly larvae cement their cases to the stones; others move jerkily about, creating the illusion that the stream bottom itself has come to life.

Adult caddisflies are inconspicuous, mothlike, grey or brown insects whose wings are scaly or hairy and are folded at a rooflike angle over the body when at rest. Some—notably the "grey flag" or "sedge," one of the few day-flying caddisflies—are known to the trout angler, who fashions his artificial flies to resemble them as closely as he can.

Also in the spaces between stones, or just under them, and in the lee of the current, there are likely to be naiads of mayflies (Ephemeroptera), which may measure up to half an inch in length. Most often these naiads are brown; all are well protected by chitinous armor and provided with large, strong legs. Like those of the stoneflies, both larvae and adults have cerci or caudal filaments; some species have two, and others three, of these backward-directed "feelers" (Figure 18).

Many aquatic insect larvae are like the rapid-stream mayflies in having notably flat bodies—a characteristic which at first glance might be regarded as a help in withstanding the action of the current. On second thought, however, and after a comparison with other species that live in standing waters, this theory does not appear to hold up; for there are just as many flattened larvae in lakes as there are in streams, and some of the flattest are those that avoid strong currents. The truth seems to be, rather, that among insects a flattened body form must have been developed primarily to enable the creature to hide in narrow cracks and crevices, on dry ground as well as under water. Furthermore, the mayfly nymphs that live in the most rapid of torrents do not show special flattening. A consideration of the turbulent

Fig. 18 Typical mayfly nymph. (From Leonard and Leonard, *Mayflies of Michigan Trout Streams*, 1962.)

currents over the bottom suggests that these would as often exert a sidewise push, or even an effect of suction, as they would a direct pressure from above, so that flattening would be of little use unless it were also accompanied by good holdfast devices. Thus, just as among the inhabitants of torrents and waterfalls, among the immature stages of stream insects, we find an abundance of such devices as hooks and suction cups, and of larval cases cemented to the bottom.

The Life of the Mayfly

The adult mayfly or "spinner" is not only the chief model for the fly-tying hobbyist, but is also one of the most elegant and beautiful of all animals (Figure 19). When it alights on a twig, standing high on its fragile legs, the up-

FIG. 19 Adult mayfly (*Ephemera simulans*). (From Leonard and Leonard, 1962.)

ward curve of the abdomen with its sweeping caudal filaments is reminiscent of the sure but delicate brush-strokes of a Chinese painting. The two pairs of wings—the first of which is much larger than the second—are both lacily net-veined; and in color the bodies and wings alike run through almost the entire spectrum of possible hues. In addition to various pigments, a mayfly's wing often displays iridescence, due not to a colored substance but to the interaction of light rays with the minute structure of the cells.

Unlike most insects, which emerge as adults from the aquatic or semiaquatic juvenile stages, the mayflies undergo another intermediary stage—that known to biologists as the subimago and to anglers as the dun. It emerges on a day when the surface of the stream is smooth and unbroken. Suddenly a small circle appears, then another and another, until the stream is dotted with them: the mayfly hatch has begun. The duns float downstream, supported by the surface film on widely pivoted legs; one by one they raise themselves above the water as they prepare to flutter toward the bushes by the shore. From above, swifts dart down, uttering faint, excited shrieks, to catch the subadult mayflies as they take wing. From below, trout are steadily rising, snapping at the insects the moment they leave their larval skins, gulping them down while they are still afloat.

In some species the dun stage lasts but a few minutes, in others a day or longer; in either event, the subimago has to shed a thin cuticle to reveal the fully formed spinner, ready to take off on its nuptial flight. The adults are invariably short-lived—the females of some species do not even live long enough to lay their eggs; they drop into the stream immediately after mating, and the eggs are released from the dying animals whose only function in life is to mate and propagate the species. Those that inhabit larger rivers and the shores of lakes often form dense clouds as they emerge in the sunset of early summer. Their spent bodies sometimes settle in drifts over roads and bridges, and the living swarms have been known to clog sewers and even to form temporary obstacles to traffic. On July 23, 1940, the Associated Press carried a dispatch that read as follows:

STERLING, ILL.—Shadflies that in some places piled to a depth of four feet blocked traffic over the Fulton-Clinton highway bridge for nearly two hours last night.

Fifteen men in hip boots used shovels and a snowplow to

clear a path. The bridge appeared to be covered with ice and snow. Trucks without chains were unable to operate until most of the flies had been shoveled into the Mississippi River.

Egg-laying in Stream Insects

Reproduction is one of the life functions that is made difficult by strong currents. Thus adult stream insects pair outside the water; but either the eggs or the larvae in an early stage must somehow reach their submerged habitat. The eggs of almost all typical stream insects are equipped with adhesive mechanisms of one kind or another. They may be covered with a sticky substance such as will easily adhere to stones; or, as is typical of many stream mayflies, the female may even go down into the water, find the right stone, and deposit an egg package upon it. A short time later, her lifeless body will float on the surface of the stream.

In early summer, small delicate female flies of the genus *Baetis*, with large iridescent eyes that glimmer like miniature lanterns, may be seen hovering over many streams. Every now and then one of them will land on a stone at the streamside, rest there for a while, and put her head and forelegs into the water as if to test it. If the current is too strong at the place she has chosen, she will be drawn in to perish then and there. Others manage to survive the plunge, during which they look like little silvery bubbles. On the way down they carry some air under their wings, where it is insulated by the dense bristles on their legs. Thanks to the supply of oxygen provided by this insect equivalent of a diving bell, a female may stay under water for half an hour or more. If she outstays the time provisioned by her initial supply, she can replenish the vital gas under water, because as the tension of oxygen within the bubble falls in relation to that of the surrounding water, dissolved oxygen from outside diffuses into the little protective air chamber and replaces what has been lost in the respiration of the insect. This peculiar system of underwater gas exchange is yet another dividend of small size; a larger animal could not thus take advantage of surface tension.

The diving caddisfly female looks for a suitable place for laying her eggs by touching all surfaces over which she walks under water with the tip of her abdomen. When she has found a spot that suits her—usually one in the lee of a stone—she curves the hind part of her body, raises her tail

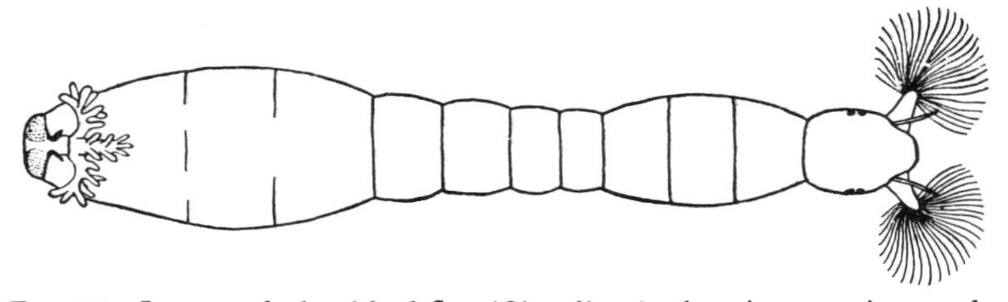

FIG. 20 Larva of the blackfly (*Simulium*) showing suction pad (stippled), gills at rear end of animal, and feathery, plankton-catching fans on its head. (From Pennak, 1953.)

bristles, and firmly attaches several irregular rows of whitish eggs to the stone. *Baetis* lays somewhere between 80 and 300 eggs—far fewer than those aquatic insects that broadcast their eggs into the stream in flight—but she compensates by making sure that the eggs are so placed that most of them will hatch.

A close look at a small pool formed by the shelter of a few large rocks, may reveal a series of pads consisting of little, curved, brownish-black rods projecting upward from the stones on the bottom. These are the larvae of blackflies, notably abundant insects in the fast-flowing waters of high mountain streams (Figure 20). Fastening them to whatever small protuberance the stone may offer is a small ring of chitinous hooks, at the rear end of the larva; it is directed downward and outward to form a circular clasp. The body of each animal stands upright, swaying with the movement of the stream and holding out two fan-shaped catchers which intercept microscopic plants and animals as they float by.

Female blackflies, like some caddisflies, dive with an air bubble to lay their eggs under water, but they do so closer to shore than where the larvae are found later on in their lives. Thus it must be assumed that the latter are capable of migrating to places where their filter-feeding habit can be used to best advantage. When the time comes to pupate, the larva uses its silk glands to spin a pointed cocoon, with an opening to the lee of the current, and attaches itself to the stone.

Before the stones one has just been examining have been replaced, preparatory to wandering downstream, some peculiar copper-colored patches on the underside of the rock may excite one's curiosity: are they animals, plants, or merely stains on the rock? Almost certainly they are beetle larvae of a kind for which the noted entomologist J. H. Comstock has suggested the picturesque and fitting name "waterpenny." Each one has a slightly raised bump in the center of its flaring segmented surface. Only when it is turned over (as it can be with a pocket knife), does it display moving legs and other insect characteristics (Figure 21). The adults are known as riffle beetles (Psephenidae); they grow to be barely a quarter of an inch long, and their bodies are clothed with hairs which allow the female to retain a film of air around her when she climbs down into the swiftest portion of the stream, just as the female mayfly does, to deposit her eggs on the underside of a stone.

Insects of Quieter Waters

Riffles are more prevalent in hill and mountain streams than in the lowlands, but rapid-flowing stretches and pools may occur almost everywhere. With their eddies and still waters, their stands of water plants, their variable bottom material, and the grasses and overhanging bushes that fringe their shores, these sections of a stream form the richest of all flowing habitats. Here a sampling of the inhabitants becomes more difficult; in addition to turning over stones, one may need some device for dredging up sand or silt, and a net to

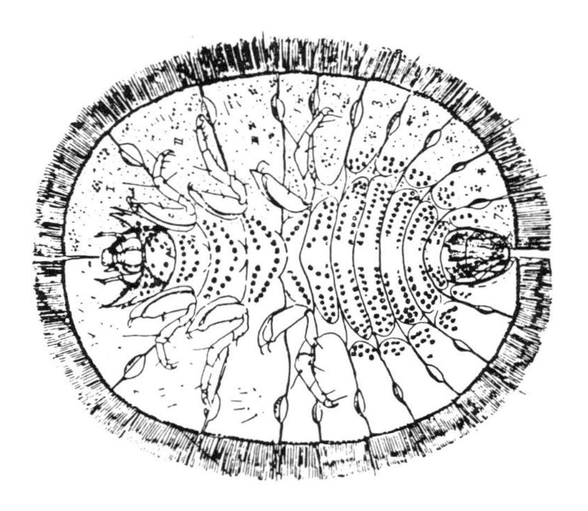

FIG. 21 Ventral view of waterpenny, the larva of a riffle beetle (*Psephenoides*). (From Wesenberg-Lund, 1943.)

catch the surface swimmers. Nevertheless, many insects can be observed by quietly sitting on the bank of any stream in spring or midsummer. Among them will be rapidly circling water bugs and beetles, and the slower-moving water striders. Beneath the surface their larvae, as well as those of predatory dragon- and damselflies and the large hellgrammite or alderfly larva—the finest of fish bait—may all be found; and there will also be planarians, snails, and leeches. The insects that are found in the rapids all have relatives that make their homes in slower water; the quiet stream and its pools may perhaps contain fewer stoneflies and blackflies, but there will be many mayflies and a great variety of caddisfly cases. Some of the naiads that inhabit these tubes capture what comes along in the stream with their long feathery antennae; others spin nets just as *Hydropsyche* does, suspending them on sticks or leaves near their homes (Figure 22). Such a net will function as a strainer

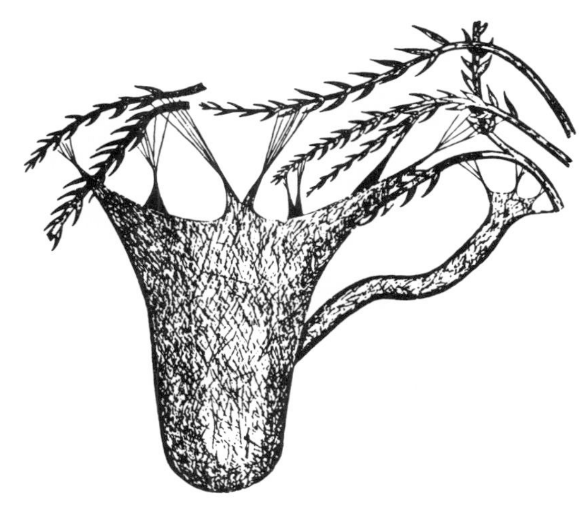

FIG. 22 Catching net of a caddisfly larva on submerged aquatic plants, with small escape passage to the right of the net. (From Wesenberg-Lund, 1943.)

only if it is clean, and the legs of the naiad are equipped with tufts of stiff, fine bristles that keep it so. The spinning of nets outside the case necessitates getting around in the current, and these caddisfly larvae have strong hooks on their legs to fit them for such forays.

Where the banks embrace a pool with blades of grass dipping into it and a canopy of alder leaves overhead, the water will be dotted with whirligig beetles (Gyrinidae) and pond skaters or water striders (Gerridae). The brownish-black, shiny beetles glide about each other in irregular paths propelling themselves with their flat, paddlelike, stubble-fringed legs. The least disturbance sends them scattering in all directions, and they will dive when alarmed—an indication that they have very good vision. In fact, the eye of a whirligig beetle is divided horizontally into two sections, the upper one normally projecting above the surface of the water, the lower placed below the antennae and looking down into the water. These beetles are good divers as well; their wing covers close to form an air chamber, just as do those of their larger cousins the predaceous diving beetles; both species are rendered so buoyant by this air supply that when they go below to feed they have to cling to the bottom with hooked forelegs.

True bugs are an insect order (Hemiptera) distinguished by a pair of forewings that are leathery at the base and membranous at the tip, and by mouthparts in the form of a piercing, sucking beak. Of the many true bugs that live on or in the water, the water striders and the backswimmers are probably the most familiar. The former are light enough to skate on the surface film, spreading their long legs to give them six widely separated points of support. In the process of evolution most of them have lost their wings and are thus strictly tied to the water, where they feed on plankton or on other aquatic insects, including the weaker members of their own species. Backswimmer bugs (Notonectidae) hang head downward from the surface of the water. They swim on their backs, gliding on smooth, keel-shaped wings and propelling themselves by regular oar-strokes with their hind legs. They also dive for their prey, again taking a silvery air bubble down with them as an oxygen supply. The heads and backs of notonectids show various patterns of yellow, grey, tan, or black. Anyone who brings off the difficult feat of catching a backswimmer is likely to receive a sharp sting that leaves a burning after-sensation.

Although less easily seen than the backswimmers, their cousins the water bugs are much larger, occasionally reaching a length of more than two and a half inches—a considerable size for any insect, terrestrial or aquatic. They are brown or green, and blend well with the stones or plants to which they cling just under the surface of the water. Their anteriorly inserted forelegs, with which they grasp their prey, are flexed like the muscular arms of a wrestler displaying himself in the ring (Figure 23). Water bugs are

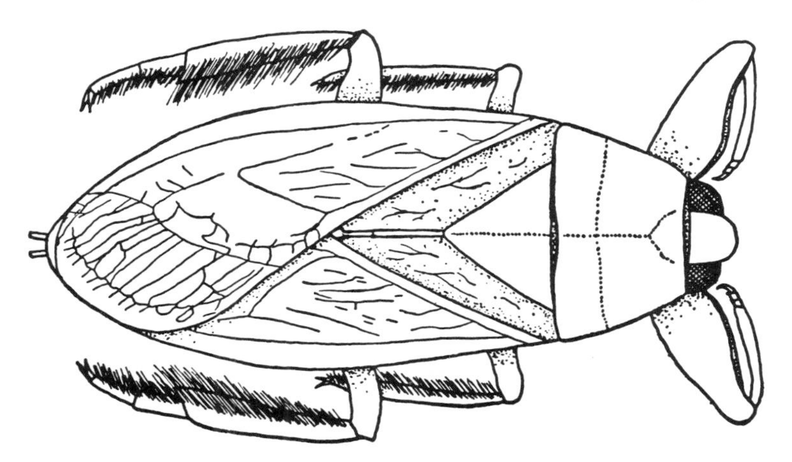

FIG. 23 Giant water bug (*Lethocerus americanus*). (From Pennak, 1953.)

big enough to capture tadpoles or fish larvae, which they kill with a toxic salivary secretion, and thus occasionally become a nuisance in fish hatcheries. The female cements her eggs to the back of the male, who carries them during the week or two required for incubation (Figure 24). Some giant water bugs (Belostomidae) occur in the Midwest and in the East, but they are more prevalent in the southern states and in the tropics.

Insects of many other orders and families spend a part or all of their lives in or on the stream. Most of them feed on plant matter or small animals, and their variety and manifold adaptations add to the complexity of the food web in many stream communities. They are generally most abundant during the summer, but some reach their greatest numbers in the winter. Streams freeze only in their slowest portions, and the water rarely is colder than 40° F., a temperature at which cold-blooded animals can carry on all life functions. There are tiny nocturnal caddisflies that

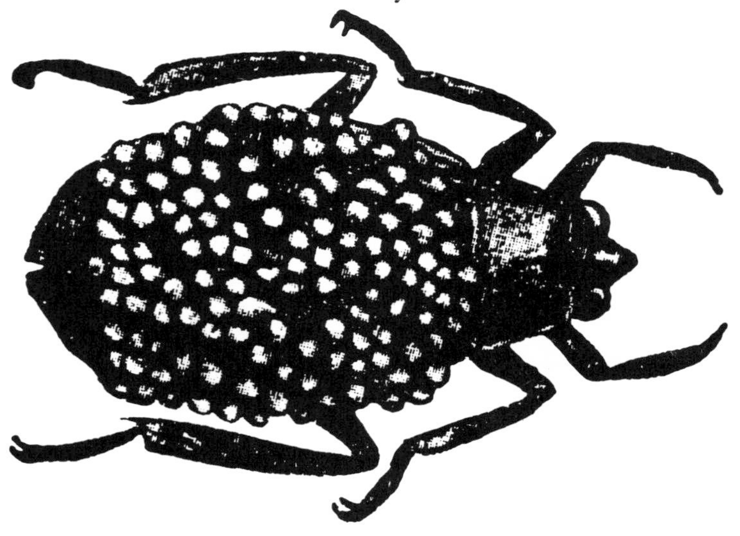

FIG. 24 Male of a water bug (*Serphus*) carrying eggs on its back. (From Wesenberg-Lund, 1943.)

hatch in early spring; certain mayfly larvae also achieve most of their growth during the winter, as do the small shore-loving water springtails (Collembola), relatives of the glacierflea. The most striking winter forms, though, occur among the stoneflies. About a third of the thirty or forty species in the northern United States emerge, mate, and feed during the coldest months of the year. They provide year-round food for fishes and for the insect-eating permanent residents among the birds, as well as for the earliest returning migrants. The adaptiveness of insects to so wide a range of conditions is one of the chief reasons why they outnumber all other kinds of animal life.

Among the varied flying insects that hover or flit above the stream and its bordering meadows or bushes, few are more conspicuous and beautiful than the dragon- and damselflies. Their squat submerged larvae (Figure 25), on

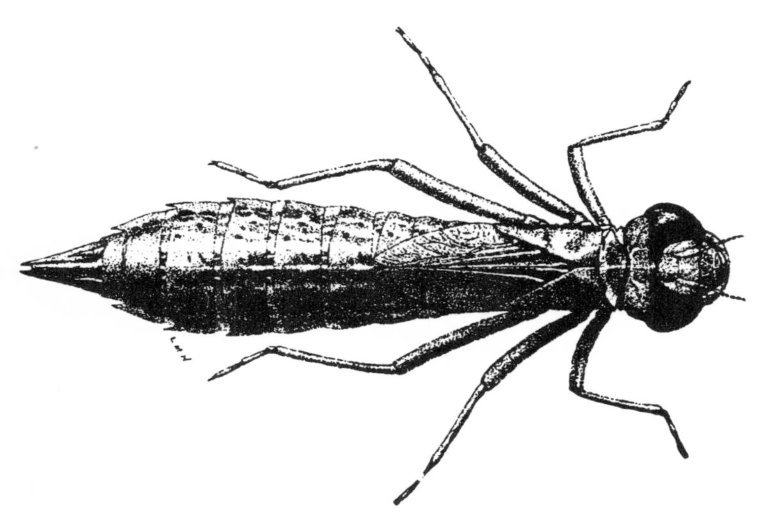

FIG. 25 Nymph of the dragonfly (*Anax junius*). (From Wesenberg-Lund, 1943.)

the other hand, are downright ugly, with formidable mouthparts and fierce-looking faces. They stalk their prey with slow, purposeful motions, and when the hapless worm or molting insect is within reach, one pair of mouthparts, the labia—also called the feeding mask—shoots out like a spring-loaded pincer to grab the prey (Figure 26). Once she has it firmly in her grasp, the nymph takes her time in crushing it with the other mouthparts and chewing it inside her gizzard.

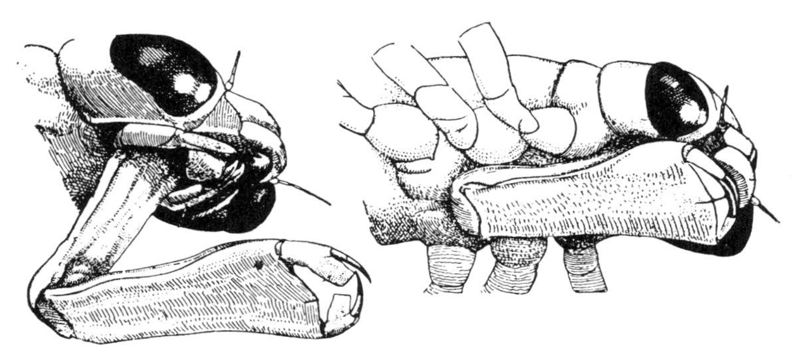

FIG. 26 Head of a dragonfly nymph. The feeding mask is shown both folded and extended to reveal grasping claws at the tip. (From Wesenberg-Lund, 1943.)

The iridescent, net-veined wings of an adult dragonfly may have a spread of four inches, and their darting flight is skillful as well as strong. The body of the insect is strikingly colored, and the huge compound eyes, occupying the greater part of the head, endow the dragonfly with keen vision and allow it to grasp its prey of smaller flying insects in the air. Looking up to see a pair flitting in nuptial flight through the warm, pine-scented air, and hearing the faint, rapid clicking of their wings, is one of the myriad pleasurable components of sitting on a log by a stream on a summer afternoon.

Mesmerized by the patterns of the water's surface almost to the point of dozing off, one is abruptly shaken out of the summer trance. Suddenly, a movement breaks the surface of the water, as first one and then another trout, rising, darts out of the pool and into the faster-flowing water. For a moment or two the fish are carried downstream by the current; but a flick of the tail brings them up again to the spot where they first appeared. For many, this endlessly thrilling sight is its own reward.

Stream Fishes

Even those who have peered many times into the strange watery world of the fishes can never cease to marvel at their varied shapes and their perfect ease, well-being, and mastery of the environment. As the largest, the most conspicuous, and therefore the best known members of the stream community, they also serve as indicators of the nature of the current.

Thus the smaller bodies of flowing water in temperate America are often classified into trout streams, bass streams, and those waters where carp and minnows abound. This is a legitimate division, reflecting such conditions as temperature, rate of flow, amount of dissolved oxygen, and so on. By implication it also suggests what plants and animals accompany the physical conditions, so that a biologist who speaks of a typical trout stream can tell, with a reasonable amount of exactness, what algae, what mosses, what snails, and what insect larvae one may expect to find there.

Fishes of the trout family (Salmonidae) have a pronounced streamlined form. Many of them have pink flesh, whose color is due to carotinoid substances in the plankton crustaceans and insect larvae which form an earlier link of the food chain. However, since their color, like their diet, is variable, it is not possible to predict whether a trout on the hook will turn out pink or white. Hatchery-raised, liver-fed trout have white flesh which can be turned pink by admixing shrimp meal to their diet.

Trout are all powerful swimmers, and their spawning

habits are geared to life in moving water. They bury their eggs in the small spaces between the stones and pebbles, where the developing fry will be protected from the current but will still have ample oxygen when they emerge as yolksac-carrying larvae. The summer water temperature of a satisfactory trout stream does not exceed 70° F. for more than a week or so at a time. Brown trout tolerate slightly warmer water than a rainbow or a brook trout (the latter of which is, zoologically speaking, not a trout but a char). Either species will perish in waters containing less than five parts per million of dissolved oxygen, but since trout waters are normally well saturated with air this is rarely a danger.

The somewhat slower, warmer streams in North America and Canada are called bass streams. These are farther from the headwaters; they have, on the average, less than a quarter of their surface shaded by streamside vegetation, and therefore the average summer temperature often far exceeds 70° F. In bass streams of a large river system of Ontario it was found that more than 30 per cent of the flowage area consisted of still waters; in a good trout stream, still waters will usually amount to less than 15 per cent.

Whereas a trout is cylindrical in cross section and has a rounded head, a smallmouth bass (*Micropterus dolomieu*), is shaped like a double wedge in cross section. It is, though, still much less flattened than the bluegill or the crappie, both of which belong to the same family. If *Micropterus* were to attempt the faster currents which a trout navigates easily, its relatively flattened body would be buffeted about mercilessly by the turbulent cross-currents of the stream. The spawning habits of bass are likewise geared to quieter waters. The eggs are laid in open depressions among coarse sand or small gravel that have been hollowed out by the males, who guard their brood until the fry can fend for themselves.

Besides the indicator species, trout streams contain a few

other kinds of fishes, and bass streams a great many others. The sculpins (Cottidae)—heavy bottom-dwelling fishes with large heads and large pectoral fins—share the colder and more rapid waters with the trout, while sticklebacks and mud minnows are often found in the quieter reaches of a trout stream. Sharing the habitat of the bass, on the other hand, are suckers, creek chubs, and a number of bottom-dwelling darters, as well as an occasional pike or perch, a few bullheads, and a great many minnows. In slower streams the fish community, like that of the insects and of the aquatic plants, is much larger than in more rapid waters; and in the sluggish streams of the lowlands, the plant and animal communities will resemble those of ponds and lakes.

Streamside Birds and Mammals

A number of higher animals make the streamside their home. The beaver, the otter, and the water shrew have come to lead an almost aquatic existence, and animal life in brooks and streams also attracts a number of birds. In eastern and midwestern North America only the spotted sandpiper, the waterthrush, and the belted kingfisher have entered into really close association with the stream, though occasionally marsh or upland birds come down to pick over the succulent grasses near the water.

The spotted sandpiper (*Actitis macularia*) is exceptional among shore and wading birds in that the members of its species live and breed near brooks and streams throughout the entire continent, instead of raising their young only in the far north, as their numerous relatives do. This is a small sandpiper, around seven inches long, greenish-grey above and white marked with large, dark, round or oval spots below. The nest, built in a depression in the ground near the stream, is lined with grass and leaves. The eggs are cream or grey, well camouflaged with black or purple blotches. When approached, any sandpiper will wag its head and body up and down in a teetering motion, alternating with short runs—probably as a sign of alarm. The little spotted sandpiper shows this habit to a marked degree, though in another habit it differs from many of its kind: instead of luring an intruder by fluttering before him on the ground as though feigning an injury, the female remains quietly on her nest until the intruder is almost upon her.

At first glance the northern waterthrush (*Seiurus noveboracensis*) may appear quite similar to the spotted sandpiper; although it is a bit smaller, it is likewise greenish-grey above and white with dark markings below; it even has the same tail-bobbing habit. On closer inspection, though, the bird is seen to be stockier, with shorter legs and a shorter bill than the sandpiper; the markings on its underside, though comparable in color, differ in outline, and there is a distinct pattern of dark and light on the head. The resemblances, even though they may possibly have come about as a response to the same habitat, are in fact only superficial, for the two species are not closely related. The sandpipers belong to the order of shore and wading birds, whereas the waterthrush is actually a perching bird of the same family as the wood warblers. Its nest, which is likewise built near the water, is better concealed than that of the sandpiper; often it is tucked under the roots of a tree that reach down over a steep bank. It is lined with moss and leaves, and usually contains four or five white eggs with small chestnut-colored spots. The bird migrates as all warblers do; it is comparatively tame, and frequently comes to gardens and feeding stations during its travels. A lucky observer may have the pleasure of hearing its melodious, warbling song.

According to a legend, the kingfishers before the Flood were drab birds; but when Noah liberated the pair he had taken aboard the ark, they flew into the sunset, and forever afterward the blue sky was reflected on the bird's back and the rays of the setting sun on its breast. Though the bird of legend was a European species, all kingfishers are colorful; found throughout the world they are most common along tropical streams, where they flash like jewels through the opening made by the water in the green monotony of the jungle. They are streambank dwellers *par excellence*, powerful flyers with keen eyesight and great skill in capturing fish and frogs, which they often spear with their beaks. Anything but a contemplative angler, the kingfisher dives from its perch on a branch of a tree overhanging the stream, or from a fluttering halt in midair above the water. The prey, firmly held in the strong beak, is taken to a tree, where it is quickly beaten to death and then swallowed head first.

Kingfishers are territorial birds, each pair fiercely guarding their fishing domain against all others of their own species. The nest is a burrow in the bank, where a colony of bank swallows are often near neighbors. There the female lays five to eight pure white eggs, which need no protective coloration since they hatch in the dark. Ordinarily kingfishers, which feed largely on minnows, frogs, and insects, with perhaps an occasional trout, are not regarded as destructive. However, when a fish hatchery is situated near a stream where a pair have chosen to nest, kingfishers can become a nuisance as soon as they discover the hatchery ponds and begin to procure their food the easy way.

Kingfishers in general have been called the Alcyones; and the name of the belted kingfisher of North America is *Megaceryle alcyon*. Both are derived from classical legend. The story is that Alcyone, a Greek princess, was so deeply grieved over her husband's death by shipwreck that she threw herself into the sea, where she was immediately changed into the bird that henceforth bore her name. Pliny's *Natural His-*

tory, in which fanciful notions and superstitions are interwoven with accurate observations, reported that halcyons were bred in a nest set upon the surface of the ocean, and hatched at the time of winter solstice, which on the Aegean Sea was a period of calm and pleasant weather—hence the expression "halcyon days."

At times when stream insects are hatching and emerging from the water, many other birds besides streamside and marsh species come to feed on them, even though they do not otherwise live in close association with the stream. Such upland birds as the grackles (*Quiscalus*) are sporadic visitors to the grassy stream borders in search of seeds and insects, even occasionally snapping up a juicy beetle larva or a worm from the water, to supplement their largely vegetarian diet. In summer these handsome black birds with jackdaw-like tails and an iridescent plumage with glinting overtones of metallic blue, green, and purple often patrol the shores of streams in flocks. On their wintering grounds in the Gulf states they also show a fondness for the water, feeding on the invertebrates that lie hidden in the mud of marshes where many ducks also spend the winter. As the stream broadens into a river, with marshes and lowlands along its banks, it becomes the habitat of many shore and water birds—grebes, loons, herons, ducks, geese, and swans. These will be described in a later chapter.

Beavers

Unique among the mammals associated with North American upland streams are the beavers (*Castor*). Their valuable pelts were an important incentive to the opening up of the continent, and their dams have frequently changed the character and in some places even the course of American streams. Once the dams are deserted they cease to function in times of high water and thus beavers have been responsible for a number of small floods. The average beaver is between three and four feet long, a third of this length consisting of the paddlelike naked tail. It rarely uses this for swimming, but relies on its webbed hind feet. Its fur is well oiled, so that the beaver can spend much of its time under water, where it is capable of swimming submerged for a distance of one hundred yards or more. The principal food of beavers is the bark of the quaking aspen, but in summer they feed as well on the succulent roots and other parts of aquatic plants.

Where the bank is high enough the beaver makes its home by burrowing a den in it. If the bank is flat, or otherwise unsuitable, the lodge is built in the stream itself. In either event the entrance must be under water and the lodge platform must be kept dry—a requirement that is the origin of the dam-building habit. Dams create a steady water level, and in pools and ponds behind them where only the surface freezes over, the beavers are able to swim in and out of their lodges at any time of year. When the water level in a beaver colony was lowered experimentally, the animals immediately began rebuilding the dam even though it was in good repair—an indication of the way in which the dam-building instinct is triggered.

Beavers fell the trees with which they construct their dams by gnawing a deep circular wedge around the trunk, usually at the height of about a foot (Figure 27). The logs are then dragged to the dam site, where they are placed with the branches facing upstream and the thick ends downstream so as to catch leaves and debris (Figure 28). Mud and such plants as reeds or cattails are used as fillers. In early autumn, when the beavers are preparing for the winter, they can be seen at dusk carrying these ingredients clutched to their chests with their forepaws while they walk upright on their hind legs. The houses or lodges have the appearance of large dome-shaped brush piles; some are as much

FIG. 27 A beaver near an aspen tree which he has felled by gnawing a circular wedge. Photo from Michigan Department of Conservation.

as five or six feet high. Inside each lodge is a platform, the beaver family's sleeping and resting place; the space will be about equal to the inside of a Volkswagen, though it will not be as high. The outer surface of the lodge is kept moist, and in winter, when brush and mud are compacted with snow and are frozen solid, the beaver house becomes an impenetrable fortress, even to a grizzly's powerful claws.

A beaver dam may be several hundred feet long but will

FIG. 28 A beaver dam, typically with the thick ends of the branches pointing downstream. Photo from Michigan Department of Conservation.

rarely be more than eight or nine feet high. Most dams are anchored to a natural buttress, consisting of boulders or the exposed roots of an overhanging tree, and built up toward the middle of the stream; but there have been reports of more intricately constructed dams–for example, a row of piles driven vertically into the stream bottom, with limbs and trees placed across these in a thatchwork fashion. The dam with its pond also provides the beavers with a storage cellar for their winter food. Aspen trees are felled in the autumn–usually before they begin to change color, while the bark is still at its succulent best–and then dragged to the pond and submerged. The cold water preserves the trees and keeps the bark juicy. Beavers are such thorough providers that untouched trees may still be found in the pond even in the spring. In order to feed on stored aspen, a beaver will leave its house, swim under the ice to the larder, help itself to a section of branch or limb, and return to the lodge to feed on the bark. The bare stick is either discarded outside or added to the lodge, if the latter needs repair.

Beavers are gregarious; a lodge may be the home of seven or eight animals, and in a few instances as many as twelve have been counted. From two to four young are born in April or May, and they stay with the parents until they are two years old. The inhabitants of one lodge will therefore consist of a pair of old animals and the young of two successive litters. In their third spring the young leave home and look for a site of their own, elsewhere along the river. Thus beavers spread quickly over a watershed; however, they are shy and disinclined to come near to human habitations. Their effects on a stream can be especially serious when they leave an area to escape man's encroachment. Then the dams deteriorate; the next strong spring freshet tears them apart, and water and debris alike rush down the valley.

Otters

Lutra, the otter, is another shy, semiaquatic mammal that frequents streams. An otter's body is longer than a beaver's but much more slender; it has a silky dark brown coat and looks like an overgrown mink or weasel—a similarity that is not surprising since all these animals belong to the same family. The otter's hind feet, like the beaver's, are webbed for swimming, but the undulating movements of his long body also help him to glide swiftly and smoothly through the water. Otters are excellent divers and are reported to be able to swim under water for as much as a quarter of a mile without coming up for air.

Otter dens lie under the overhang of a bank, stoutly

framed by large roots and so situated that their tenants can slip almost directly into the water. The otters feed on fish, and the riffles near the den may be so littered with fish bones and skeletons as to form veritable kitchen middens. In streams where there are trout, these fish naturally make up a fair portion of an otter's diet; but like all voracious carnivores he is not particular about what he eats. Besides fish he will eat snakes and crayfish, and will not disdain even a large insect or a frog if other food is scarce. In winter, when the stream is partially frozen over, otters make foraging journeys to rapids or waterfalls, where the open water permits them to catch their food.

The otter's life history is incompletely known because of the animal's secretive habits, but pairs have been observed in the spring with two or three young, who evidently learn to swim almost as soon as they can walk. The female is reported to take the young on her back when they are ready to go into the water, allowing them to become accustomed to their new element before she lowers herself gradually, letting the babies use their hind feet while they still have some support, and finally diving out from under them so that they are left to swim by themselves.

A unique habit of otters is the building of slides on a steep bank by a pool. They clear away trash and debris and hollow out a shallow ditch that is used in the same way as a chute into a swimming pool. In the winter the slides are built in the snow; southern otters—whose range extends into Louisiana—build them of clay. When an otter is ready for a ride it tucks under its forepaws, lifts its nose into the air, and plunges head first into the water below. The game is repeated again and again, always by a group of otters; there appears to be no record of a slide being used by a solitary otter. There is also no indication that the use of the slide has anything to do with mating behavior; the animals apparently play the game purely for the fun of it. If the adjacent bank is too steep to climb, they will go back to the slide by a circuitous route, returning again and again for hours at a time.

The Water Shrew

Among other mammals that are good swimmers, the mink takes some of its food out of the water; the star-nosed mole pursues insect larvae in streams and ponds; and one of the smallest of all, the voracious water shrew (*Sorex palustris*), lives near streams and depends almost entirely on aquatic animals for food. All shrews are tiny, as mammals go; few species exceed three inches in length, including the tail. Their small size coupled with warm-bloodedness gives all shrews an enormous appetite. The smaller an animal is, the greater the exposed surface in comparison with its mass—a relation that can be envisaged in terms of three cubes measuring one, two, and three inches respectively. The surface-to-volume ratio of the first of these will be 6:1; of the second 24:8, or 3:1; and of the third 54:27, or 2:1. Because of this disparity small warm-blooded animals lose heat much more rapidly than larger ones. A shrew, in order to keep its metabolism at the high level required to offset the loss of heat, will eat several times its own body weight of insects in a single day. After only a few hours of fasting, a shrew of the very smallest species will become too weak to eat even if it should find food. However, the American water shrew is larger and apparently less delicate than many other species.

Wet places near the shores of rushing mountain streams, and peat bogs near beaver meadows, are favorite habitats of the water shrew. It is an excellent swimmer, thanks to the webbed bases of its disproportionately large hind feet and to its bristle-fringed toes, which transform the feet into efficient paddles. A water shrew is less agile on land than in the water, where it can turn almost on the spot, thanks to yet another set of bristles on the underside of the tail, which is thus transformed into a rudder. The pelt consists of closely set hairs, so fine that during a dive tiny air bubbles adhere to their tips and keep the animal dry; it looks like a minute silvery submarine as it plunges down to hunt for insect larvae in the gravel at the bottom of a clear pool.

In contrast, the pelts of otters and beavers have a different adaptation for keeping their wearers dry; both animals have a fine underfur interspersed with many long, somewhat stiffer guard hairs, and their skins contain highly active oil and wax glands. During a dive the guard hairs form an oily insulating cover, to which no air adheres; under water the animal appears dark (Figure 29), rather than silvery like the water shrew.

Shrews will eat anything in the way of animal food: fish many times their size; tadpoles, worms, larvae, the naiads of whatever insects they may find, and also the eggs of trout —or so it is presumed, since shrews have been caught in small wire traps baited with spawn. The shrew's large food requirements raise a problem in providing for the young. Water shrews usually produce from six to eight young at a time, and they may raise more than one litter in a single summer. The rapidly growing young probably need even more food for each ounce of body weight than the adults. Konrad Lorenz reports, in his book *King Solomon's Ring*, that young water shrews cannot eat adult shrew food until they have reached about half the size of the mother. If they had to rely on their mother's milk during that time, the shrew's milk production would have to outdo by far that of a grand champion dairy cow. It is Lorenz's suggestion that the mother may feed her young on pre-chewed, regurgitated food.

How do water shrews hunt their prey? The answer to

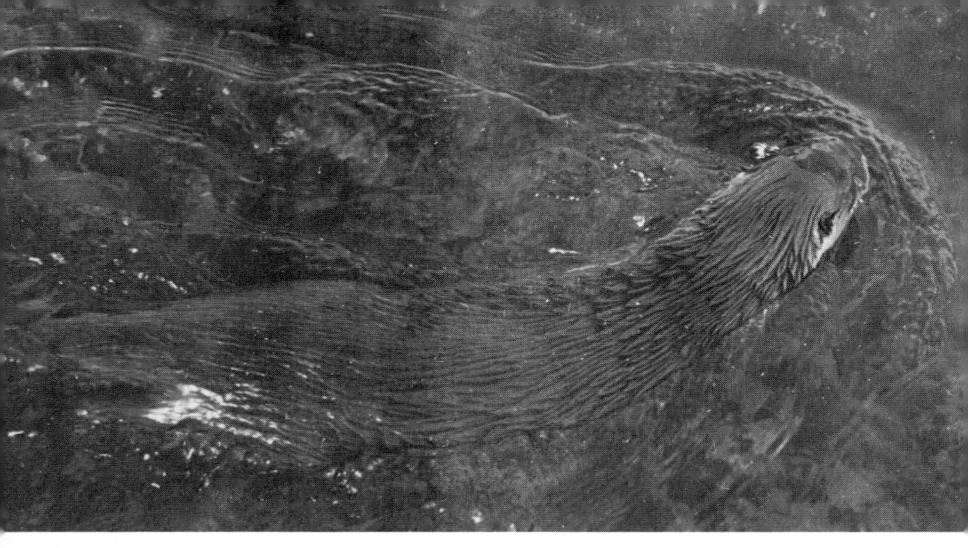

FIG. 29 A swimming otter appears as a dark streak in the water because no air bubbles adhere to its well-oiled fur. Photo from Michigan Department of Conservation.

this question is still a matter of debate. Their eyes are small, and it is doubtful whether they have very good vision. Furthermore, they are so much like their fully terrestrial relatives as to warrant the assumption that their eyes are better geared to aerial than to underwater vision. Many fishes—sharks are one instance—locate their food by their sense of smell; others, such as bullheads, use both smell and taste—indeed, bullheads have taste buds much like those of the human tongue scattered all over their bodies. But the shrew's sense of taste, like that of other mammals, is confined to the mouth, which under water remains closed except at the instant of snapping up the prey. Similarly the shrew's nose, like that of any other mammal, is fashioned to detect odors in the air rather than in the water. Apparently, however, it does have a well-developed sense of touch, which may serve for the location of its prey. The pointed nose of the water shrew is crowned with a set of stiff whiskers projecting like multiple antennae. Lorenz, a wizard animal keeper, once brought off the difficult feat of keeping eight little shrews alive in a tank for several months, and has watched them closely. He believes that they do not have to touch their prey but can detect the presence of another animal with their whiskers, simply by picking up vibrations from the water.

The problem remains, however, that such a method of hunting would be difficult in flowing water since even the smallest turbulence might easily cover up the minute displacements of water produced by a swimming prey. Shrews, which are remotely allied to the bats, have high-pitched voices, quite probably with frequencies beyond the range of our own hearing. Thus it is conceivable that the shrew may use sound to locate its prey as a porpoise does. If this hypothesis were to be verified, it would be another example of how life in the water has led to comparable evolutionary adaptations among aquatic animals, whether they live in fresh water or in the sea.

PART II.

The Journey to the Sea

4

Rivers

AN ORDINARY GEOGRAPHIC MAP REVEALS MUCH ABOUT THE action of moving water, as well as about the geology of the landscape through which it flows. Indeed, the two are inseparable. Where rivers and their tributaries follow courses that are essentially parallel (Figure 30, center)—as they do, for example, in the mountains of Pennsylvania—it may be inferred that the landscape consists of a series of tilted layers in which hard materials alternate with others that are softer and less resistant to erosion. A trellislike pattern, in which the streams shift here and there to flow at right angles to themselves, occurs where there are joints or faults in the ridges that confine the valleys. A striking example is the Delaware Water Gap, where an old, wide valley is intersected by a steep-walled break in Kittatinny Mountain. In regions such as the Black Hills of South Dakota, where the remains of ancient volcanoes form dome-shaped elevations, the streams flow away in a radial pattern, like the spokes of a wheel (Figure 30, right). Where the earth's strata are horizontal, as in central Africa, or where hard crystalline rock lies at the surface, as in northern Canada, erosion will simply follow the incline of the land. In such areas the pattern of rivers and their tributaries is dendritic (Figure 30, left)—that is, it resembles the veining of a leaf or the branching of a tree.

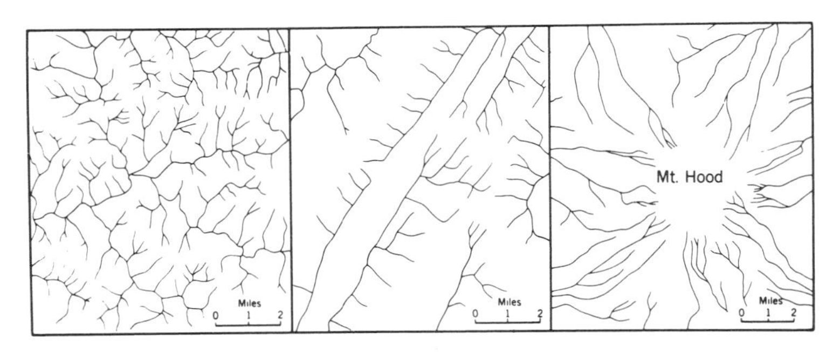

FIG. 30 Drainage patterns of rivers. *Left*, Dendritic drainage, West Virginia; *center*, trellis or angular drainage, Pennsylvania; *right*, radial drainage, Oregon. (From Zumberge, *Elements of Geology*, 1958.)

No map, however, can show the ceaseless process of change which has produced such patterns as these, and which is continually altering those same patterns with the downward movement of water toward the sea. Rivers are continually cutting back their valleys toward their headwaters, deepening and widening their beds and evening out differences in gradient. Where the slope is gradual and the material composing the streambed is homogeneous, this tendency will produce the placid aspect of a mature river farther and farther upstream. But where a river flows from a region of hard into one of softer bedrock, what happens is exactly the opposite: a series of rapids will occur where

FIG. 31 Erosion pattern of a waterfall. The plunge basin is the result of the falls' upstream displacement. Photo from Michigan Department of Conservation.

the two formations meet, and as the softer material is eroded away the gradient will become steeper and steeper, until the rapids become a waterfall (Figure 31). The most familiar example of this development is at Niagara Falls, where a hard horizontal layer of limestone overlies a very soft shale. Even now, the swirling currents in the plunge basin below the falls are sapping away at the shale, having undercut the limestone above it ever since the end of the last glacial period, thus causing it to collapse and tumble down, with the result that the Canadian falls are being displaced upstream at a rate of more than three feet a year.

The origin of many precipitous mountain waterfalls such as those of Yosemite also dates back to the glacial period, when the valleys of major rivers were often cut much deeper than their tributaries by the load of moving ice. When the ice retreated, the tributary valleys were left hanging, sometimes hundreds of feet above the ice-scoured bed of the main stream.

Rapids and cascades do not inevitably turn into waterfalls. Where a streambed is crossed by zones of hard rock, the water will simply leap from ledge to ledge without forming a vertical escarpment; and where this happens, pieces of harder rock may eventually be plucked out by the current and give rise to whirlpools. Cascades of this sort are common along the eastern seaboard from New England to Georgia, where the many rivers traversing the Appalachian piedmont enter the sandy coastal plain. Here they cut more deeply than they do into the harder substrate of the piedmont; and as a result, a series of rapids and waterfalls occur along a narrow band, known as the "fall zone," that marks the line of contact between the two geological formations.

Just as waterfalls and cascades are typical of the interplay of moving water with the underlying rock in the humid Northeast, canyons are typical of the arid plateaus of the Southwest. There, streams that have their rise in the snows of the high mountains have carved deep trenches into the relatively soft limestones and sandstones and then into the underlying crystalline rock. The Grand Canyon of the Colorado is only one of the many bizarre and spectacular results of the massive erosion that occurs when swiftly moving water encounters materials that are easily moved.

Obvious features on any map are the divides that separate one watershed from another. What the map does not show, once again, is the continuous change in the watersheds themselves. Where, as frequently happens, one slope of a divide offers less resistance to erosion than the other, the rivers will cut back their valleys at a faster rate, and may eventually divert into their own channels the headwaters of rivers that rise on the opposite slope. At several points in the Appalachian region, this piracy or "beheading" of one stream by another has transformed a onetime water gap into a dry pass, known as a wind gap. The most famous of these is the Cumberland Gap, through which tens of thousands of settlers led their covered wagons into the wilderness of Kentucky and Tennessee.

In some ways, viewing a landscape from a plane is a more satisfactory way of understanding the force of moving water than looking at a map. This is especially true of flying over mountains, deserts, and other thinly populated regions. Elsewhere, however, the results of slow-moving natural forces have been overlaid, modified, or even obliterated by changes that are largely man-made. Nowhere is this more true than along a large river, where a complex of dams, levees, shipping, railroads, and highways have often drastically affected the natural habitats and the communities of plants and animals that once lived in its waters and along its shores.

Truly undisturbed rivers are now rare, except in the Arctic and in some tropical regions. But here and there in our own part of the globe, river habitats may be found that preserve something like their pristine condition. Such an enclave has been set aside in the Upper Mississippi River Wildlife and Fish Refuge, which stretches intermittently for nearly three hundred miles through bottomland marshes, sloughs, and wooded islands.

Wildlife Along the Upper Mississippi

From its source in Lake Itasca the Mississippi flows northeast in an unhurried curve, then swings south through a shallow valley, where it is fringed alternately with stands of bulrushes and of mixed forest. A little farther along, as it traverses the floor of an ancient glacial lake, it develops meanders and oxbows. Still farther downstream, where it has cut a gorge through a glacial moraine, traces of braiding occur, and an occasional stretch of rapids marks its passages over a sill of harder rock. Some miles to the south of Minneapolis, an ancient widening of the river bed, known as Lake Pepin, is now stabilized by a dam. Below this the Mississippi enters a wide valley bordered on either side by steep, wooded bluffs—a phase that continues along the boundaries between Minnesota and Wisconsin southward as far as Missouri.

Where the Wisconsin River and the Mississippi meet they form a network of interlacing channels and backwaters. Here sandbanks have been taken over by trees and formed stable islands much like those downriver near Hannibal, Missouri, that are commemorated by Mark Twain in *Huckleberry Finn.* Just as at Hannibal, there are open sloughs, edged with stands of reeds and rushes (along with wild rice, which does not grow far south of Wisconsin); and likewise much of the valley is covered with lowland forest—elm, ash, and swamp oak on relatively dry ground, and birch, cottonwood, and willow near the river channels. Of the thick vines in the understory of the river forest mentioned by Mark Twain, botanists since his day have listed woodbine, grape, moonseed, hog peanut, clematis, bittersweet, and of course poison ivy as the predominant creepers of the lowland forest. In the dense ground cover of touch-me-not and other moisture-loving smaller plants berries grow profusely just as they did on Jackson Island, where Miss Watson's Jim lived for days on wild strawberries.

Dead trees that have fallen against their living neighbors here and there obstruct the channels so completely that an explorer by canoe or rowboat must pull his craft across before he can penetrate farther. Fallen or leaning trees often expose a bright spot where the sun penetrates the leaf canopy, and there an occasional turtle can be seen basking on a stump; at the approach of an intruder it will stretch its neck high into the air for an instant and then plunge into the water with a splash.

In June the light in these forests of the valley floor is subdued even at midday, and the air is heavy and still. The muddy brown water is full of fish, most of which anglers regard as trash species—suckers, buffalofish, carp, bowfins, and gars, with a sprinkling of gizzard shad and some catfish and crappies. In some years seining an acre of such waters may yield upward of five hundred pounds of fish. There will be many good-sized but harmless water snakes; some swamp rattlers still occur, and off the beaten path, among the rocks that must be scaled to reach the oak-covered bluffs, timber rattlers may also be encountered.

In spite of the mosquitoes—which are bothersome even during the day and become a major nuisance in the evening—it is worth the trouble to stay on (armed with insect repellent) through the dusk, when the river lowlands truly become alive. Bird calls become more frequent, and a rustling of leaves here and there betrays the presence of other animals. The first form to appear by a little sandbank will perhaps be that of a raccoon (*Procyon lotor*); in the fading light it is still possible to make out the black mask surrounding its alert eyes, as well as the pointed white snout tipped with a jet-black nose, and the long, bushy, black-ringed tail (Figure 32). Raccoons, although not restricted to wooded river bottoms, are partial to such places. The dens in which they sleep away the days, and where they hibernate for a part of the winter, are usually in hollow trees, but one may sometimes be found in the dry crevice of a cliff, an old fox burrow, or even a deserted muskrat house. A raccoon as it forages for acorns, nuts, fruits, insects, and crayfish, now and then taking a crippled young waterfowl, often prowls along watercourses, where it may even capture an occasional fish. Raccoons have the habit of washing their food—whence their species name *lotor*, or "the washer"—and of sitting up on their hind legs, inquisitively scanning their surroundings.

FIG. 32 Raccoon washing its food. Photo from Michigan Department of Conservation.

As the raccoon disappears, a muskrat (*Ondatra zibethica*) emerges, sniffs, and silently follows a path into the water that might have been overlooked but for the appearance of the big chocolate-brown rodent (Figure 33). It swims away in the dusk with the top of its head barely emerging, leaving a wedge-shaped wake as it steadily paddles with its large, webbed hind feet. There is no telling whether it is bound for a feeding platform somewhere near by in the reeds or returning to a bank-burrow farther up or downstream. Muskrats build houses in the marsh that are somewhat like those of beavers, but without damming

FIG. 33 Muskrat emerging from the water. Photo from Michigan Department of Conservation.

up streams. These lodges consist of cattails and rushes plastered with mud; some of them serve as dens and others merely as feeding stations. Muskrats are prolific: an acre of suitable marsh may accommodate from twenty to forty rats, and a mile of overgrown streambank may house more than a hundred. Unlike another native furbearer, the mink, muskrats cannot be raised on farms, though by controlling the water level their marshes can be managed for optimum numbers; thus all muskrat pelts sold in America come from animals trapped in their native habitat.

Perseverance and luck may even yield a glimpse of a mink (*Mustela vison*) along the river channel, since the mink preys mainly on muskrats, principally along the banks of streams and ditches or along the shores of lakes. The chance of catching sight of a mink is the greater because of its hunting habits: ordinarily a wary and secretive animal, when it strikes it is bolder about coming out into the open than its relative the weasel.

A single mink will patrol several miles of shoreline in quest of young muskrats and of other lowland mammals, as well as birds. An excellent swimmer, it will also take fish, and in a pinch will stoop to a meal of crayfish, insects, or frogs; when it comes upon a brood of chicks or a family of mice it will kill wantonly. A trapped mink will defend itself fiercely, and will bite off its own toes in order to escape.

Until recently, lowland forests along the upper Mississippi still harbored bobcats (*Lynx rufus*), whose large hunting territories included both timbered bluffs, interspersed with sunny glades, and swampy bottomlands; and it is possible that some of these elusive predators are still there today. A bobcat looks like an overgrown tabby with a short-nosed, kittenlike face, but it will be two or three times as large as a large domestic cat and may weigh twenty pounds or more. A bobcat's legs are thicker than a housecat's and its furry ears are tipped with tufts of hair (Figure 34). It is likely to betray its presence only during the mating season, when bobcats break forth at night into eerie yowling and meowing, lower pitched and infinitely more awesome than anything even the biggest tomcat is capable of.

As the moon rises over the river, throwing the backdrop of the trees into silhouette, the gurgling of the water is punctuated by an almost endless succession of rustling and crackling noises, thrilling testimony that most mammals are nocturnal. Suddenly the small movements are frozen into silence by a booming reverberation, which is recognized with fear as the call of the barred owl. Half the size of the great horned owl, likewise an occasional hunter in river lowlands, the barred owl (*Stryx varia*) has an even more

Fig. 34 Bobcat resting near its den. Photo from Michigan Department of Conservation.

resonant voice. Among birds of prey it is the one most truly typical of the swamps. Although it is not often seen at close range, a bright campfire may attract a barred owl to a perch in a nearby tree, making possible a blurred impression of the brown-and-white crossbars of its boldly patterned plumage. More often a barred owl is seen silhouetted overhead as it combs the swamp, along with the marshes, for whatever mammals may be stirring. Its slow wingbeat and frequent changes of direction are typical of the flight patterns of all owls. The barred owls of the upper Mississippi migrate short distances south for the winter, coming back in early spring to build a nest in a hollow tree or on top of one that has been deserted by a hawk or a crow. Owls and hawks usually nest singly, but other large birds of the river lowlands, such as the great blue heron (*Ardea herodias*), gather in spectacular nesting colonies. Since the herons, of which the blue is the largest, feed primarily on fish, they do not overwinter in regions where the waterways are covered with snow and ice. It is not necessary to wait for dusk to see a great blue heron—an arresting sight as it moves slowly through the shallow water, carefully lifting its long legs and peering down with each step, its rapier-like bill poised for a strike. The neck is bent into an S-curve so that an unwary fish or frog can be speared quickly and with precision. The diet of the great blue heron is not restricted to aquatic life; pocket gophers, ground squirrels, and field mice are also greedily devoured whenever they are found. In fact, before migrating south in the fall a heron family with four or five young may eat as many as fifteen gophers a day.

The nests of a heron colony are built in the treetops of a secluded swamp. Often there will be two or three of these bulky structures woven together of twigs, branches, and dry grasses in the same tree. The young are fed by regurgitation and grow rapidly into juvenile birds that are as large as the adults, and that are ready to migrate with the parents when the weather turns cold. The body plumage of the youngsters still differs from that of the adults in being brownish rather than slate-blue, and they have neither the long black crest nor the white forehead of the full-grown bird. A heron colony may have more than a hundred nests, to which the birds often return year after year. A visit to a heronry just before the young can fly is a fascinating experience; but it is wise to go protected by washable rain gear and a broad-brimmed hat.

A number of other birds nest in the lowlands along the

river, and ducks and geese pause there during their spring and fall migrations. The wood duck (*Aix sponsa*), one of the few waterfowl to enter the woods, actually builds its nest and raises its young in hollow trees of the lowland forest, often at a height of twenty feet or more above the ground. All young ducklings are able to swim or walk as soon as they are dry, whereupon the mother leaves the nest and calls her brood; in answer the ducklings one by one struggle over the rim of the nest and plunge straight into the water. Young wood ducks are called upon to be still more courageous; when, a day or so after they hatch, their mother leaves the nest and calls to them from below, they must leap down to the ground from a height of as much as forty feet. They are so light that they rarely are hurt as they plummet onto a soft bed of grass or leaves. Once on the ground they follow their mother in single file to the nearest slough or pond.

Sometimes, when the nest is far from the water, both ducklings and adults may forage for nuts and acorns in the woods, as well as for insects, worms, or other small forms of life. After the nesting season the wood duck families apparently stay together, traveling in flocks or sunning themselves on a log, either preening their feathers or asleep with their bills under the wing coverts. The male wood duck, easily the most colorful of American drakes, has black cheeks below a crested helmet of iridescent green, strongly set off by white lines; the body plumage and even the beak are likewise multicolored. Once alarmingly rare, wood ducks are one species that artificial propagation and protection have been able to save from probable extinction.

Even close to the railroad tracks, where diesel trains cause the marsh to tremble many times a day, many wild animals persist in the lowlands along the river's edge. In refuges like that along the upper Mississippi they tolerate the noises and smells of civilization so long as they are not molested further, and it may not be long before their kind are to be found nowhere else.

River Invertebrates

The plant and animal communities within a river vary with the current, the temperature, and the nature of the substrate, just as they do in any smaller stream. In general, though, there are few floating algae in a large river, and rooted water plants occur only near shore and in slow-flowing side channels. Whereas in a mountain stream the stones shelter small animals both from the current and from predators, in many parts of the river—especially in stagnant pools and oxbow lakes, where conditions resemble those in a pond—plants serve for the attachment of many invertebrate animals and their eggs and larvae. In rivers where plants occur only at the edges, however, and where the bottom consists of sand or silt rather than stones and pebbles, burrowers will predominate.

As in smaller streams, the nature of river-bottom deposits varies with the speed of the water. In general, the finer the bottom material, the smaller the burrowing inhabitants will be. Where there are patches of fine silt or mud, worms will abound, and in stretches of fine gravel and sand there will be many mussels. A stretch of slow-flowing but reasonably clear water, especially one in which a widening in the bed slows down the current still further, is ideal mussel habitat. In and near Lake Pepin in the upper Mississippi, beds containing as many as fifty mussels per square yard were once observed. Malacologists—zoologists who specialize in the study of mussels, clams, and snails—have not fully explained the reason for the extraordinary density of these beds.

Fresh-water mussels with common names such as "fat mucket" and "pocketbook" (*Lampsilis*) are truly American animals, and key members of the fauna of many rivers. Although mussels occur all over the world, they are believed to have originated on this continent, very probably in the region drained by the Mississippi. Fossil evidence, and the greater density of species here than anywhere else, make this conclusion likely.

Mussels, clams, oysters, and scallops are bivalves of the molluskan class Pelecypoda—a name that means "hatchet-foot," and is a reference to the shape of the muscular organ which serves the animal for locomotion and, typically, for anchoring itself in the sand. The shell secreted by a bivalve consists of three layers, the innermost of which is smooth and shiny; the face of a "pearl" button cut from a mussel shell consists of this layer. The shell is actually a secretion of the outer layer of the animal proper, known as the mantle, which covers the visceral mass and lines the inside of the shell. If a foreign body, for example a parasite or a sand grain, becomes lodged between the shell and the mantle, it is eventually surrounded by the mantle secretion and a pearl is formed. Though the pearls of commerce are the work of oysters, which live only in the sea, fresh-water mussels also produce pearls. At the turn of the century many New York pearl houses had buyers in the town of Muscatine on the Mississippi, where a thriving mussel fishery was the source of shells for making pearl buttons.

A mussel lodges in the sand, from which between a half and a third of its body projects (Figure 35). The two shells are slightly open, just enough to allow special protruding structures to pass a steady stream of water through the animal. In an aquarium it can be demonstrated, by gently placing some carmine dye or lampblack with an eyedropper just above a mussel, that water is drawn into the body cavity through an incurrent opening or siphon. Almost immediately the dye will be ejected in an excurrent stream beside the intake, thus showing how the animal feeds and breathes.

Water is drawn in by means of ciliary action on the gills, which lie just inside the mantle cavity. Oxygen is exchanged for carbon dioxide, mainly on the mantle surface but also on the gills, and then the water is expelled. Any food organisms that are siphoned in—algae, diatoms, protozoa, and the like—are retained in the gill mucus and propelled by cilia toward the mouth, which is at the foot end. The anus

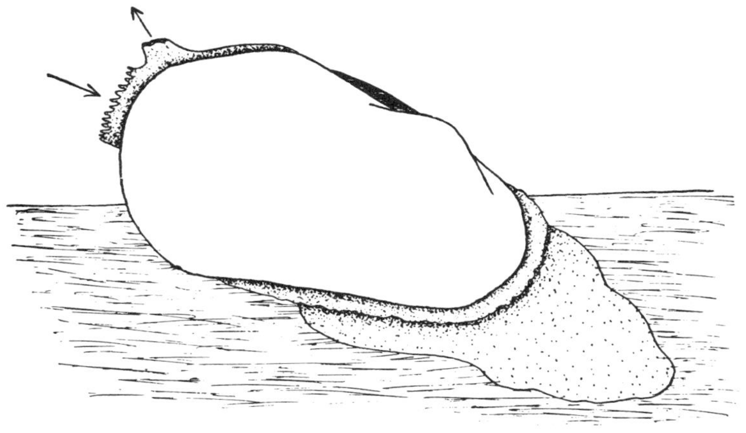

FIG. 35 Mussel in its natural position in the river bottom. The arrows indicate the inhalant and exhalant siphons. (From Pennak, 1953.)

lies near the excurrent siphon—an arrangement which ensures that the feces are carried to the outside of the shell.

When conditions around it become unfavorable, a mobile animal has a chance to escape and may perhaps survive somewhere else. When a river becomes polluted, the only defense possible to a bivalve mollusk is to close its shell and dig in deeper. After a while it must open up again, though, since it will need to inhale water for breathing, if not immediately for feeding. Thus pollution will quickly hit oyster and mussel populations, as will increased loads of silt, which tend to smother the animals and prevent them from respiring. In what were probably the densest mussel beds anywhere in the world, those of the upper Mississippi, not only was there heavy exploitation, but the animals had to contend with increasing domestic and industrial pollution, as well as silting caused by man-made changes in the river. In the interest of shipping it was desirable to have a deep, navigable channel as high upstream as possible. To this end dams and locks were built which also produced electric power. There are now twenty-six such dams and navigation locks between Minneapolis and St. Louis. As a result the flow of the water has become so slow that it can carry in suspension only the very finest silt or colloidal particles. All the rest settles, some of it on the mussel beds.

The peculiar reproductive habits of mussels also have turned out to be a handicap. Like most other sessile animals, bivalves in their larval stages are either free-swimming or capable of attaching themselves, in the manner of a hitch-hiker, to some other, more mobile animal. The latter is exactly what the mussel larva does. Female mussels produce hundreds of thousands, if not millions, of eggs that hatch into larvae, are expelled, and slowly sink to the bottom. Of these only a relative few survive, by attaching themselves to the gills or the fins of a fish, where for a few months they live almost as parasites. Then they transform into small adults and drop to the bottom. The parasitic mussel larvae are called *glochidia* (meaning "point of an arrow"). When their preferred host fish declines in number, the mussels follow suit. Furthermore, after transforming into adults they run the additional risk of not finding themselves on the right kind of bottom for their comfort. It is no wonder that bivalves are among the most fecund animals known; their survival would not be possible otherwise.

Certain mussels have developed extraordinary lures for tricking fish into visiting them and thus unwittingly into receiving a load of glochidia. When the female of the species *Lampsilis ventricosa* is ready to spawn, her mantle develops a fleshy papilla in the region of the siphons (Figure 36). The papilla assumes the shape of a minnow, com-

FIG. 36 Mantle flap of the mussel (*Lampsilis ventricosa*) simulating a moving minnow. Photo by Dr. John H. Welsh in *Science*.

plete with a black spot corresponding to the eye, as well as a gently fanning tail fin. A passing fish will come close to investigate, and as it swims over the object that has aroused its curiosity it is bombarded with mussel larvae. A comparison of *Lampsilis* with some of her relatives gives a striking example of adaptive evolution at work; for some of the latter have no lures and others have a small thickening of the mantle where *Lampsilis* develops her fish-attracting device. The genetic mutations that have produced this lure must have been in operation for millions of years. Indeed, they are still in progress; as each of the strains that can produce "false fishes" just a bit more deceivingly than another correspondingly attracts more fishes as potential glochidia-carriers, it thereby propagates its own kind with greater success.

Not only have mussels taken advantage of fishes to carry their young; precisely the reverse situation occurs in the bitterlings (*Rhodeus*), a genus of Old-World minnows, several species of which lay their eggs in the gill chambers of mussels. The fish is at most three inches long, and is found in the slow-flowing side channels of many European and Asiatic rivers. During the winter males and females swim together in large schools. At that time few or no mussels are in evidence; they have burrowed deeper into the river bed and disappeared from sight—a fact that led some earlier biologists to believe that they made seasonal migrations. In the spring, when the water warms up and the days become longer, the mussels emerge again and extend the upper part of their shells out of the fine gravel, using their siphons more and more vigorously. The male bitterling, a silvery little fish during the winter, now takes on an iridescent rosy sheen; his fins become fringed with black, and on the tip of his snout appear two pinhead-sized, white, hard knobs, the breeding tubercles. The female's color hardly changes, but she grows an egg-laying tube which will enable her to insert her eggs into the inhalant siphon of the mussel. The tube, which she trails behind her, is transparent, soft and pliable, and measures two to three times the length of the female bitterling's body.

The males now become highly interested in the mussels. One after the other, as they reach breeding readiness, the males each stake out a territory around a mussel and defend it against other bitterling males. Fin up, each one swims alertly around his chosen area, occasionally making a swift sidewise sweep over the future cradle of his brood. This apparently habituates the mussel to the presence of the fish, for soon the shells stay open despite their normal tendency to close at the least hint of any movement near by. It is also believed that the fishes' chafing stirs up debris containing minute organisms, so that the mussel derives some benefit from its passive acceptance of the bitterling's eggs.

Whenever another male bitterling approaches, the resident male attempts to head him off by swimming in circles between the intruder and the mussel. If that fails, he resorts to more vigorous tactics. As the two contenders swim side by side, the resident begins jerking violently, so as to direct a strong wave against the lateral line of his opponent. This manner of showing strength is a feature common to the duels between two fighting males of many fish species. It may suffice to convince the intruder that the resident is the stronger of the two and that it might be better if the other tried his luck elsewhere. If the two males are evenly matched, the side-sweeping and tail-beating may give way to a head-butting contest, in which the hard knobs of the breeding tubercles come into play. If head-butting is of no avail, the resident will resort to biting and nipping. In most instances of territorial defense, among bitterlings as among other animals, the resident has a psychological advantage over the intruder and generally retains control of his little realm.

Usually after a fight—and also at other times—the male will sweep low over the siphon area of the mussel, occasionally expelling sperm as he does so. Before the sweep he stands immediately over the siphons, head down as though closely inspecting this strategic area. But when a female with a well-developed laying tube passes through the weeds around the mussel, the male behaves quite differently. He swims up to her, circles, and then, in a slow zigzag motion that displays his iridescent sides, leads her toward the mussel. When they are directly above it, first the male and then the female go several times into a head-down position. The female in particular seems to be trying to locate the incurrent siphon. As soon as, with uncanny aim, she has inserted her laying tube into it, the tube itself stiffens, and along with a squirt of urine an egg or two is expelled into the gill chamber (Figure 37). The tube thereupon becomes flaccid again and the female swims away, retracting the tube

FIG. 37 Female bitterling investigating siphon area of a mussel, depositing an egg in the mouth cavity of the mussel, and withdrawing her laying tube. (After Wiepkema, *Archives Neerlandaises de Zoologie*, Vol. XIV, 1961.)

as she goes. Now the male sweeps again and again above the mussel, each time releasing a little white cloud of sperm over the inhalant siphon. The stimulus for sperm ejection may be either the sight of the female depositing her eggs or the odor of the urine that has been promptly expelled by the siphon. The female will return to lay a second and occasionally a third batch of eggs in the gills of the same mussel—rarely more often—before she finally swims away. Soon her laying tube is almost completely reabsorbed, to reappear three or four weeks later when a new batch of eggs has developed. Meanwhile the male waits for another female or two and then leaves the mussel, from which a dozen or more bitterling larvae finally emerge. The bitterling fry have absorbed nourishment from the yolksac in the safety of the mussel's shell, where they are protected from the vicissitudes of the larval stage, which is so extremely hazardous that more than 99 per cent of the free-living fish larvae in any waters have perished before it is over.

In places where the river flows so slowly as to accumulate silt or even mud, bivalve mollusks will no longer be found. Instead, the boring and digging bottom-dwellers will consist largely of small worms and insect larvae that feed on protozoa and organic debris, or of others that filter the ooze in order to extract whatever nutrients they may find there. Certain aquatic relatives of the earthworm, known as sludgeworms—especially those of the genera *Tubifex* and *Limnodrilus*—fall into this category. These worms can survive low oxygen concentrations because like certain midge larvae they possess hemoglobin, the oxygen-carrying red pigment that occurs in human blood cells, and which is believed to help these animals to take oxygen from the water more efficiently than their colorless relatives. As the supply of oxygen decreases, the animal comes farther and farther out of its tube, meanwhile waving its body more and more violently. Colonies of such worms look like soft cushions covered with dense, pliable red threads. They occur not only in rivers but also in the oxygen-poor bottom waters of eutrophic lakes. When the oxygen in the water has disappeared completely they retreat into their tubes, where they become inactive and where the hardier members of the colony evidently can survive for between eighty and a hundred days without any oxygen at all—although just how they accomplish this feat is as yet unknown. From the standpoint of human welfare these hardy organisms are important because their presence is generally a sign of pollution, which will be treated more fully in a later chapter.

River Fishes

One of the few generalizations that can safely be made about river life is that the bigger the river, the bigger the fish it will contain. As any angler knows, sizable brook trout occur only in good-sized streams, and the home of the brown trout—a bigger fish than either the brook or the rainbow trout—is in still larger bodies of water. By the same token, the great rivers of the world are the homes of the biggest fresh-water fishes—such giants as the rapacious Nile perch, the Mekong catfish, the Columbia squawfish, the arapaima of the Amazon, and the sturgeons and their relatives in the Volga and the Yangtze. These fishes all thrive in big rivers—or rather did thrive, since they are nearly all less abundant now than they once were. Fishes can grow big in rivers not only because they have space to grow in but also because all the way downstream the fertility of the river is being increased by new material from its tributaries, and from the drainage of the land around them. In addition, many of these large fishes extend their ranges still farther by migrating, either within the river system itself or between it and the ocean, in order to deposit their eggs.

One of the most interesting of these river giants is the

paddlefish (*Polydon spathula*). Like the sturgeon, it belongs to a group of fishes at once primitive and specialized, with cartilaginous skeletons similar to those of sharks. Only two species of paddlefishes are in existence today—one in the Mississippi and the other, which attains an even greater size, in the rivers of China.

Paddlefishes measuring six feet and weighing almost two hundred pounds were caught in the Mississippi as recently as 1900, when they were still being fished intensively; even today one is taken now and then, though it is never as big. The back and sides are slate-grey, and the underside is milky white; the fins of a mature fish are tinged with salmon-pink. There are traces of scales only on the upper lobe of the caudal fin, the rest of the body being naked. The outstanding feature of the species is a flat, paddlelike snout, as much as a quarter to a third of the length of the body. The snout begins to appear when the fish is a month old. Just what use it is to the fish is still a matter of controversy. Possibly soft mud may be dug up with it during the quest for food, although normally the fish feeds while swimming with its mouth open. The snout weaves continually back and forth as minute crustaceans are swept into the mouth and sent on into the gullet, while long gill-rakers allow the water to pass out over the gills. Thus it has been suggested that the snout may serve as a food detector, which would then presumably be equipped with special sensory structures. According to still another theory it may be a stabilizer developed in synchrony with the body shape and with the large mouth, which is often kept open in swimming. As with so many relatively unfamiliar animals, much of the paddlefish's life history remains obscure.

In fact, although as long ago as the sixteenth century members of the De Soto expedition had told of catching in a net "the Pelefish, destitute of scales with the upper jaw extended in front a foot in the form of a peel or spatula," no one ever saw the spawning of the fish until 1960, when Charles Purkett of the Missouri Conservation Commission observed the phenomenon in the Osage River. The female made a spawning "rush" over a gravel bar, expelling eggs while rapidly agitating her caudal fin. She was accompanied by several males, who released milt beside her. The water level of the Osage fell a few days later, exposing the bar and revealing that the fertilized eggs had developed a strong adhesive coat, which kept them attached to the pebbles; they hatched seven days later. The decline of the Mississippi paddlefish since 1900 is attributed mainly to the building of dams on the upper river; these have meant more silt and fewer of the sand and gravel bottoms which are the animal's preferred spawning sites. A once heavy commercial fishery for the species probably also contributed to their decline in numbers, especially after the dams had changed the water regime of the river.

Of the family *Acipenseridae*, the sturgeons are more widespread and better known than their paddlefish relatives, and for many centuries their flesh has been considered a delicacy. Prized by the Greeks, sturgeon was reserved in China for the table of the emperor, and at Lucullan banquets in Rome it was brought in garlanded with flowers. The roe, when specially extracted and salted, becomes caviar. The sturgeon is a prolific fish with especially large ovaries; there is a report of one old female weighing 3000 pounds and containing 800 pounds of eggs. The huge fish spend their adult lives mainly in the ocean, but come into rivers to spawn and–it is reported by Russian zoologists–to hibernate as well. They are then to be seen through the ice in ten to thirty feet of water, standing with their heads buried in the mud and with their tails projecting from it like a forest of poles. The pointed snout and the prominent barbels on the lower jaw suggest that the sturgeon may find much of its food by digging for bottom-dwelling life, though it has also been seen to chase other fishes; in fact, after examining the stomachs of many thousand sturgeon, Russian biologists have concluded that fish become increasingly important in their diet while they are in the sea, slowly reaching sexual maturity and preparing themselves for their spawning journey into fresh water.

Sturgeon are probably the longest-lived of all known fishes; some have supposedly reached the ripe old age of a hundred years. Even if these reports are exaggerated, it is a fact that the female of the large Russian sturgeon, the beluga, first returns to spawn at the age of eighteen years, the males becoming sexually mature at fourteen—all of which suggests that sturgeon must grow old indeed, compared to other, smaller fishes. Though remarkably little is known, altogether, about the maximum age reached by fishes, the longevity of a species appears to be a function of size. Most minnows have a life span of from two to four years; perch older than seven or eight years are rare; lake trout in northern waters probably do not live much past the age of fifteen; and even carp, despite their reputation for longevity, seldom exceed two or three decades. In comparing the maximum ages and the growth rates of various fish species it must also be taken into account that tropical fishes tend to grow faster, mature earlier, and die sooner than temperate-zone and northerly species. But even when this caution is observed, the longevity of the sturgeon remains surprising. Their age as a taxonomic group is also impressive; the sturgeons of today are scarcely less primitive than their fossil remains, dating back 120 million years, and indeed their bony heads and armor-plated sides give them a prehistoric appearance.

Catfish, another typical group of river-dwellers, have notably poor eyesight—even as fishes go—but are endowed with an exceptionally acute chemical sense. They have taste buds not only on their barbels—the fleshy "whiskers" that have given them their name—but on other parts of their bodies as well, including the tail. In laboratory experiments a blinded catfish will veer around immediately if a few drops of meat juice are gently released near the tip of its tail, and will begin a frantic zigzagging search for food. Because they can also survive where the oxygen supply is low, catfish are well adapted to live in warm, turbid waters such as are found in many big rivers. Some species have also invaded the mountain torrents of South America and Asia, where they brave the current with the special sucking attachments described in the third chapter.

Even today, Mississippi fishermen occasionally report catfish weighing a hundred pounds or more. These are most often the so-called "blue cats" (*Ictalurus furcatus*), big specimens of which were so common before 1900 as not to be worth mentioning. But even the largest of these cannot compete with the giant catfish (*Pangasianodon gigas*) of the Mekong in southeast Asia, which may be over nine feet long and which truly suggests a small whale. Like most catfishes it is scaleless with a white underside; the color of the back may be anything from brown to blue-black. It has tiny eyes, and the large mouth is equipped with rasping teeth which are lost in old age; it feeds mostly on algae attached to the streambed, and on whatever small animals may find shelter there.

The Mekong arises among the mountain glaciers of Tibet, turns south through a narrow valley in the Chinese province of Yunnan, and flows through Laos, Cambodia, and Vietnam on its way to the South China Sea. There are many widenings and narrowings, and consequently many rapids, along its varied course; and especially in Laos and upper Cambodia, many reaches contain the deep pools that are the home of the giant catfish. When the native fishermen, after long and patient watching, discover a catfish in its lair they surround their quarry and—if they are lucky—haul it in with a strong net. In a country where fish makes up most of the sometimes scanty protein diet, the capture of a giant catfish or two is an occasion of rejoicing.

Although only scattered facts concerning the life history of this great fish are known, it seems likely that only adults inhabit the upper reaches of the river, where they may live to be fifty years old, possibly even older. Though of a comparable size to some beluga sturgeon, they do not quite reach the age of the latter; most probably that difference is due to the sturgeon's distribution in temperate waters rather than in the tropical streams that are the habitat of the Mekong catfish—an example of the effect of temperature on the growth rate and the life span of fishes. Lurking in deep hollows at the bottom of the river, they are safe from the flood waters that hurtle down the Mekong every year during the monsoon rains. It seems probable that they spawn toward the end of the high-water season, and that the larvae are carried down to the lowlands, where they are believed to develop into sizable fishes before making the journey upstream.

As might be expected concerning so spectacular a creature, especially in a region where spirits and demons abound, there are many legends connected with the giant catfish. It is said that only the females wander freely over the river, while the males (whose reputed golden scales are clearly a figment of the imagination, since *Pangasianodon* is scaleless) await their arrival in Lake Tali, far to the north in Yunnan, whose waters they never leave. A journal of the Natural History Society of Siam once contained an article implying that the female nourished her young with milk! The conservation measures that must be taken if this unique fish is to be preserved are difficult to carry out because they would require not only the presence of trained scientists, in an area where such men are scarce, but also the cooperation of officials and fishermen of several countries that are not currently noted for working together closely. And because of an impending scheme to regulate the yearly rampage of the Mekong and its tributaries, somewhat along the lines of the TVA, the days of the giant catfish may be numbered. Once the scheme goes into effect, the journey upstream will be blocked by dams, the deep pools where the catfish live will be obliterated, and the huge nursery areas that are inundated by the Mekong every year will likewise vanish.

The giant among fishes that spend their lives in fresh water is the pirarucu or arapaima (*Arapaima gigas*) of the Amazon and the remote rivers of the Guianas—a species that may reach twelve feet in length and three hundred pounds in weight. Until recently it occurred in such large numbers that its life history might reasonably be expected to be known in some detail. But information on its habits, food, and migrations is still scarce, and like the Mekong catfish, the arapaima is the subject of superstition and legend; for instance, some credulous people believe it suckles its young.

A spectacular fish in every way, the arapaima is covered with scarlet scales, each one as big as the palm of a man's hand, overlaid with an iridescent glitter of blue and purple. Teeth are borne not only on its jaws but on almost all the bones of its mouth and palate. The head is flattened, but behind it the huge body is laterally compressed like that of a bass.

During the low-water period the arapaima lives in the main river channel, but when the rainy season begins it migrates upstream into a bayou or backwater, presumably to spawn. It betrays its presence by a peculiar sounding leap, from which it drops back tail first like a tarpon. By the time the rains are falling steadily and the crashing leaps of the arapaima are to be heard, the natives of the region have made ready canoes, drying platforms, and weirs, all designed to trap the great fish. Some are taken with hook and line, some with spears, and others with bow and arrow. In order to transport them back to camp, a canoe is filled with water, placed under the fish and bailed out until it and its burden are afloat. The flesh of the arapaima is to the inhabitants of the upper Amazon what beef is to those of central and southern Brazil. To prepare it, the fish is cut open along the back, the backbone is removed, and the muscles are sliced into thin strips many feet long, which are then salted and dried. These are tied in rolls, to be either shipped downstream or stored for jungle trips by the tribesmen themselves. On the Peruvian Amazon the canoes of travelers are commonly supplied with a roll of arapaima (which in Peru is called paiche), together with a cooking pot and a bunch of green plantains or a bag of beans or rice. In the heyday of the paiche fisheries, before the advent of kerosene, oil for lamps was also extracted from the arapaima. From time immemorial its toothed tongue and other mouthparts have been used in South America as wood rasps and graters for cassava root.

In the more populous regions the arapaima has already become extinct, and it is scarce over most of its range. It has been taken in enormous numbers, and what laws exist for its conservation have been largely ignored. But it is probable that the chief reason for the decline of the arapaima, as of so many other giant fishes, is in the changes wrought by man, both on the watersheds and in the rivers themselves.

Life Along an Arctic River

The number of rivers that may still be described as undisturbed is rapidly dwindling. Even in tropical Africa, the landscape and the waters that drain it are coming increasingly under the influence of man. In South America, although a like pattern will no doubt eventually prevail, vast primitive stretches still remain along the Amazon and the

Orinoco. The same is true of northern Canada, where majestic rivers support a community of large game animals, predators, and birds whose lives go on much as they have for thousands of years.

The Thelon, flowing through the districts of Mackenzie and Keewatin to empty into Hudson Bay, is such a river. Like the Mackenzie and the Coppermine, among others, it has its rise in the bogs of the northern spruce forest, from which it enters the tundra, carrying into its valley a finger-like extension of forest habitat for a distance of fifty miles or more. In such a valley there is shelter from the wind that blows almost incessantly over the tundra—sometimes gently, with a singing sound, more often with the driving force of a gale. Thus the trees that have no chance of becoming established on the uplands may do so in the valley. Even here they are small and slow-growing, often gnarled and twisted like those on mountain tops; and only the hardiest species, chiefly spruces, can gain a foothold.

The north, with its forests and tundra, has not only the same trees as the high mountains but also the same flowering plants and many of the same animals as well. In both environments the ground is frozen for a part of the year, with intermittent superficial thaws, and snow falls in the winter instead of rain. The flowers of both regions have short stems and large heads, and are often very colorful; nearly all are pollinated by insects rather than by the wind. Most of the land animals hibernate or leave at the onset of cooler weather, but in both regions there are some that remain active, and whose pelts or plumage change in color from grey or brown to white—for example the snow grouse or ptarmigan and the varying hare.

Another striking parallel between the high alpine and arctic regions is to be found in the zooplankton of lakes and ponds. Species with resistant winter eggs have had the best chance to survive in both climatic zones, and many of them

—especially the copepods—show a striking red and purple coloration in their adult stages. A sampling of either a high alpine or a tundra lake will reveal myriads of the tiny shrimplike creatures, all more intensely colored than the reddest of deep-sea shrimp. Their color, like that of the flesh of salmon and some trout, is due to carotinoid substances; just what adaptive value it serves, however, has not been fully determined.

But the parallel between the two environments cannot be extended indefinitely. In the Arctic, largely because of its greater remoteness, animals flourish that are not to be found in the mountains farther south. Wolves (*Canis lupus*) have all but vanished from the United States; but they continue to thrive along the rivers of the Arctic, where they prey upon ground squirrels, mice, and ptarmigan, and may now and then snatch an unwary goose. They commonly have their dens among the roots of a clump of scrub spruce, in a dunelike patch on the brow of a slope overlooking both the river and much of the surrounding terrain. In color they range from creamy white to almost black. During the arctic summer, when food is abundant, a wolf may often be seen dozing in the sun. At the approach of a human intruder it will merely blink, lick its nose, yawn, and lie down to resume its nap, and campers are seldom disturbed except by the howling of wolves at night—though in winter this might be a different story.

But the most spectacular inhabitants of the Arctic are the great browsing mammals, the muskox and the caribou. In fact, the Thelon River is unique in providing the last stronghold of the muskoxen (*Ovibos moschatus*) on the entire American mainland. During the ice age, herds of these horned mammals ranged as far south as Missouri; but the warmer climate drove them north into the tundra, where they remained undisturbed until the latter part of the nineteenth century. Then, as a market developed for their hides, which were sold as sleigh and carriage robes, they were wantonly decimated by Eskimos who had been equipped by traders with rifles for the purpose. Sizable herds of musk-oxen still inhabit the islands in the Arctic Ocean; but by 1927 the last mainland herd had dwindled to a total of less than fifty. In order to protect this remnant, the Canadian government set aside an area of 10,000 square miles along the Thelon as a game sanctuary, and here the muskox herd had increased to more than two hundred when a count was made in 1952.

The muskoxen are relatives of domestic cattle, and are about the same size—the cows being somewhat smaller and the bulls sometimes a bit larger. Both are dark brown except for a creamy line along the backbone, with coats of long hair which appear, especially in the bulls, to fall straight from the shoulder to the knee, and which incongruously suggest the skirts of a hula dancer when the animal is running. The horns of the bulls, which curve down and then forward from a plate in the center of the forehead, are much heavier and more rugged than those of a domestic bull. The cows have smaller, daintier horns, which spring from the sides of the forehead.

The tundra, the ancestral home of the muskoxen, is a bleak place in winter; but even then they are able to break through the crust of ice and snow with their hoofs in order to feed on the sparse remnants of moss and grasses. During the summer's respite from the long months of almost complete darkness, the tundra is alive with a lush growth of grasses, sedges, mosses, lichens, berries, and dwarf willows. But since the most succulent plants of all grow near the river, its banks are their favored summer feeding places, and the muskoxen follow them tenaciously during the summer migration downstream to their inland wintering grounds.

The abundance and variety of the food supply, and the

somewhat milder conditions in the protection of the valley, are not the only reason why it is the preferred summer haunt of the muskoxen. What is perhaps equally important, the river banks are best suited to the staking out and defending of territories which are a part of the yearly ritual of mating. The many green swales, bordered by trees and by the river itself, seem made for just this purpose. Here, at mating time, a bull without a herd of his own will establish himself. When an old bull approaches with his cows, the holder of the territory will challenge him in an effort to take the harem away from him. Like most such combats, the contest between the two males is highly ritualized. It begins with snorting and pawing and the rubbing of horns against a boulder or the trunk of a tree. As the two bulls approach one another they circle for position, marking time like wrestlers; then, after backing away a few steps, they rush at each other with lowered heads, colliding with a thud that can be heard half a mile away. They push but do not gore each other as each one tries to stand his ground and to drive the weaker one out of the ring. Finally the contest is decided; and either the old bull takes his herd on downriver toward the next tournament, or the challenger takes over all or part of the herd.

Young bulls that still travel with the family group often engage in mock battles, which show no less clearly how well the instinctive fighting behavior ensures that the strong shall have the first chance at reproduction while no bodily harm comes to the weaker. Movements, stance, and position determine whether a fight will ensue, and even during a bout one of the contestants may call a halt simply by disengaging himself and retreating; whereupon both the juvenile combatants go peacefully back to their grazing. The same kind of jousting between males occurs among deer and elk, and among fishes, lizards, and snakes as well. It is a serious but not a deadly business; injury occurs by accident rather than by design, as for instance when two elk cannot disengage their antlers and as a consequence both die of starvation.

The muskoxen do use their horns for defense against predators, though, and it would appear that they are not easily harmed by an enemy. In one herd of thirty or more a cow was observed that had survived to adulthood with a withered foreleg—testimony to the effectiveness of the herd's communal defense system. When it is attacked, in winter especially, a herd forms a circle resembling a wagon fortress: the older animals stand outside, heads down, with horns bristling, while the younger cows and the calves remain within. Only a desperate pack of wolves would be likely to attack such a circle; instead, their usual habit is to isolate the weakest stragglers and bring them down one by one.

Unlike the muskoxen, the caribou (*Rangifer arcticus*) cross the river on their migrations. After wintering in the forests south of the tree line, they head in summer for the high, windy ridges of the tundra, in order to escape the insects that swarm in lower and more sheltered places. Caribou are evidently powerful swimmers, holding a steady course against even a strong current, with only their antlered heads and their white tails showing above the water. As they emerge they shake themselves much as a dog does, scattering spray in every direction. Their shed antlers may be found lying here and there about the tundra, many of them with signs of having been chewed by the caribou themselves, presumably to satisfy an instinctive hunger for calcium and phosphorus.

A herd of caribou blends remarkably with the grey-green expanse of the barren lands, so that a visitor to the region may find himself surrounded by them without any previous inkling of their presence. The effect is all the more startling since a full-grown bull may have antlers the height of his own body. Caribou are inquisitive animals, and will approach a man in order to inspect him closely. Their eyesight is said to be poor, however, and their apparent fearlessness of man may simply be due to their mistaking him for another caribou.

Traces of caribou hair about the dens of wolves are evidence that the latter do take some caribou—probably stragglers from the herd. A still larger predator, the barren-ground grizzly, likewise does not disdain caribou meat when he can get it. This largest of all barren-land animals does not stray far from the river, where its trails and scats may occasionally be seen; but unlike its cousin the Alaskan brown bear, it is very shy as well as uncommon. The expedition in 1952 to count the muskoxen in the Thelon game sanctuary was fortunate enough, though, to bring back the first photographs ever taken of this subspecies of *Ursus horribilis*, whose second name describes him very well.

Above the river, beside a stony patch fringed with blueberries and other small, shrubby plants, the great bear came into view as he lazily stood up on his hind legs and sniffed the air. His fur was the color of creamy coffee, shading to dark brown on the belly, on the insides of the legs, and on the lower jaw. Standing upright he rose to a height of between six and seven feet; on all fours he would have measured perhaps four feet. He had a prominent hump, small yellow eyes, and a noticeably triangular muzzle with prominent jowls. Curious about what he evidently took for a new kind of caribou, he came close enough for the explorers to have an uncomfortably distinct view of his long, sharp, formidably curved nails before he caught a whiff of the unfamiliar scent, realized his mistake, and took to his heels.

Geese, Swans, and Other Birds

In addition to mammals along their shores, in summer the Thelon, its tributaries, and the many lakes through which it flows, all teem with birds. Each year many ducks, loons, grebes, terns, jaegers, Canada geese, and whistling swans return from their southern wintering grounds to this summer paradise for water birds. Here they build their nests, lay their eggs, and hatch their young; and here they molt and renew their feathers before the fall migration takes them south once more.

Molting geese and ducks cannot fly, and since on land the likelihood of falling prey to a wolf or perhaps an eagle is great, they spend this period in the open water. They keep warily together in large flocks; the older, more experienced birds, which have returned to the same region for several summers and have thus probably encountered man, are the most easily alarmed by an intrusion. A boat drifting around a bend in the river will raise a soft cackle among a flock of molting Canada geese (*Branta canadensis*), several of which are always on the alert. As these scouts give the alarm call, the cackling becomes more vigorous, and first one and then another of the entire flotilla will begin beating its wings as if about to take off, until the river fairly churns with geese skimming over the water's surface. Although during the molt they cannot raise themselves into the air, by means of rapid paddling and wing-strokes they can move through the water with considerable speed. Early in the morning, when the twilight of the short summer night brightens into the vivid light of the long arctic day, the geese come ashore to feed. Wherever they have concentrated, a level strip of wet meadow will be left clipped of every blade of grass and sedge, as cleanly as though a power mower had passed over it. Even then the geese never venture farther than fifty yards inland: some are always on the alert, and most of them "talk" incessantly to each other. As the sun rises higher they go back to the safety of the open water.

The Thelon also flows through the nesting country of

the whistling swan (*Olor columbianus*). Usually these great birds choose the shores of lakes along the tributaries, rather than the main stream, and an explorer in search of a pair may have to travel several miles on foot before he happens upon them. He does have the advantage that on leaving the river valley he has also left the trees behind and can thus see for miles. In such a landscape a white swan or two will stand out from a great distance, and can be spotted easily. But the advantage works both ways: the swans will almost certainly have seen him too, for their vision is extraordinarily keen. The best the observer can do is to sit down, remain as motionless as possible, and watch the nesting pair through binoculars. He will see the female sitting on the nest while the male stands guard near by; as soon as the observer moves, he will become agitated, raise his neck, and begin patrolling up and down. The nest itself consists of a mound of mosses and lichens with a depression in the center. When the female leaves the nest, she covers the eggs with an insulating layer of moss so as to keep them warm.

In August, after the eggs have hatched, the females begin bringing their cygnets to the river. The young birds, as the story of the Ugly Duckling testifies, are greyish brown at first, becoming lighter as the fall approaches; and they grow very rapidly. The males, no longer tied down by guard duty, will sometimes appear alone on the river. It is believed, though, that the families stay together during migration and perhaps even throughout the winter.

The birds most frequently seen along the Thelon are gulls, terns, and wading birds such as sandpipers. In a braided section of the channel the downstream edges of small temporary islands, and gravelly shores where grasses and sedges grow, will be thick with nests. Among the terns (*Sterna*), each pair of which has a small territory, there is much coming and going and much ritual threatening and posturing, accompanied by a great deal of noise—expended in defense of the limited breeding space and the one or two tiny, golden, black-speckled chicks—whenever an intruder appears. Nor is this mere bluffing; a tern will swoop down and attack, with uncanny aim, anyone who ventures too near.

Sandpipers (Scolopacidae) exhibit another kind of parental bravery: it starts with the feigning of a broken wing, fluttering on the ground in a spiral or zigzag motion, apparently aimless and without direction, just ahead of an unwitting trespasser. It is soon evident, though, that the tacking course of the bird is always away from the nest—which was, of course, in the grassy hummock out of which it first appeared. At a distance of thirty paces, the "broken" wing seems to be healing, and at a distance of fifty the bird can fly again. As it takes off it is still flying away from the nest, but it soon banks and returns to settle down upon its eggs.

Arctic Food Webs

The food web in the country along an arctic river is peculiarly simple. With the exception of the birds that come to breed there during the summer, the number of larger resident land animals is small. There are a few hibernating rodents, such as ground squirrels and lemmings, and there are snowshoe rabbits and willow grouse to provide the staple food for the predators—which are mainly wolves, with some arctic foxes and an occasional barren-ground grizzly. Population changes among the herbivores—especially among the lemmings with their famed four-year cycles—are promptly reflected in the number of wolves. Farther south, in the zone of tension between the northern spruce forest and the tundra, rodent fluctuations also affect the numbers of lynx and snowy owls.

It has been said that the Arctic lends itself particularly

well to the study of ecology; for a clear-cut schematic outline of the relations between predator and prey species can be gained there better than almost anywhere else. In most habitats in the temperate zone, and certainly in the tropics, there are dozens of herbivore species in a niche where there is only one in the Arctic. Consequently there are also more species of predators; for if one kind of prey is reduced in numbers there will always be another one to fall back on, and thus violent fluctuations of predators are rare.

These relations prevail not only on the land around an arctic river but also in the river itself. In the Thelon, as in many rivers in the same latitude, the lake trout (*Salvelinus namaycush*) is the top predator. In contrast to its habits in more southern waters, and belying its very name, the lake trout in the north comes to the surface readily and is found in the larger streams and the main rivers.

It is possible to stand on a projecting gravel bar that has been formed by a stream flowing into the Thelon, and, by casting into the eddies, hook several lake trout in rapid succession. One is almost certain to catch the biggest fish first, and one need not be surprised if it measures three feet in length. Continued casting produces progressively smaller lake trout, but even these will rarely measure less than eighteen inches. It is almost as if the smaller trout did not dare to take the bait while the largest and presumably the senior member of the territory is still about. Anyone who has fished under such conditions, hooking six or seven good-sized fish in fifteen or twenty minutes, is spoiled for life. The reason for the good fishing along the Thelon is, of course, that one is more likely than not to be the first man ever to cast a lure into the water in any one spot.

Besides the lake trout, northern pike also occur in the Thelon and its surrounding lakes; they too may reach considerable size—a length of two or three feet is not unusual. Like the lake trout they prey on the lower piscine ranks in the food pyramid, consisting of several species of whitefish that are mostly plankton- and bottom-feeders. Like trout, to which they are closely related—in fact, they belong to the same family—whitefishes are believed to have radiated into arctic and alpine waters during and after the last glacial period. Some whitefish species feed mainly on snails, others on copepods; and still others rely on the young of other fishes for sustenance. There are few fish species of smaller dimension in the Thelon, or at any rate few have been reported from the very scanty sampling that has been done there. The only species found were some sculpins and the three-spined stickleback, but it is not known to what extent these enter into the diet of the larger fish-eating predators.

In the Thelon lakes some whitefish species, such as the inconnu (*Stenodus leucichthys*), grow to a length of over two feet; they are then too large to fall prey even to the largest lake trout or pike, especially since they grow as strongly in height as they do in length. Once they have reached that stage in their lives, they may attain the ripe old age (for a whitefish) of twenty years or more, unmolested by the predators with which they share their aquatic habitat. In this they are somewhat comparable to the musk-oxen, whose size, among other factors, helps to make them relatively immune from wolves, bears, and other larger terrestrial predators.

Because of its harsh climate, among other factors, the Thelon country has a better chance than almost any other region of continuing as the domain of wild animals for generations to come. During the summer their abundance exceeds even that of the animals in some tropical sanctuaries; and since there are no known mineral deposits and little likelihood that any will be found, since the soil will not yield any crop, and since there is no other inducement for settlement along its shores, the Thelon will quite probably remain what it is now, a wilderness river virtually unaffected by man.

5

The River Meets the Sea

A RIVER NEARING THE END OF ITS COURSE FLOWS MORE and more slowly through its broad valley and over the flood plain its waters have been gradually laying down for thousands of years. The melting glaciers, the mountain brooks and springs, the forested slopes, the lakes in which it has tarried, the bluffs along its middle course—all have been left behind. Even before it reaches the sea, the rhythmic counter-pressure of the tides may be felt far upstream. A hint of fog or a whiff of salt in the air gives tangible evidence that the last destination of all moving water is near at hand.

As a glance at a map will show, a river may end in one of two very different ways. The mouths of such rivers as the Hudson, the Thames, and the Loire, on the one hand, have the form of deeply indented bays and estuaries; those of the Mississippi, the Nile, and the Orinoco, on the other, are built outward into triangular deltas. This striking difference is an indication of gradually shifting adjustments in the earth's crust. Where the level of the coastline is rising or is relatively stable, sediments carried outward by the river will be deposited more rapidly than they can be dispersed, and a delta will form; where the shore has subsided, the river mouth will be an estuary. A further complication is added by the rise of the sea, which has been steadily under way since the melting of the last glacial ice cap began.

Estuaries

A simple estuary—the mouth of the Seine is an example—has the shape of a funnel and gives free access to the tides; but where the drainage pattern of the land produces the confluence of several rivers at or near their mouths the estuary becomes more complex, with ramifying channels, bays, and marshes—as in Chesapeake Bay. Tides and currents produce sandspits that partly close off the river's mouth; they may even form the long, low islands known as barrier beaches, that run parallel to the shore and protect mile after mile of inland waters—as has occurred along the Atlantic coast southward from Long Island. Here lie vast shallows where river and ocean waters are mixed by the influence of the tides, which pass through gaps in the bars and barrier beaches. Along these estuarine shores, where high tides regularly give place to low, mudflats and the plant and animal communities peculiar to them come into being.

Mudflats

The rigorous but varied environment produced by intermittent exposure to the tides and alternate bathing by salt and fresh water consists of a series of intergrading zones, each with a character of its own. In the shallows below the tide, eelgrass (*Zostera*) may form dense underwater meadows. The common name is not apt, for despite their appearance these plants are not grasses at all, but pondweeds (Najadaceae) that have developed a high tolerance for salt water. Much of their rapid spread is due to underground rootstocks, and even in cooler climates the blades remain pale green throughout the winter. Eelgrass meadows are excellent hiding places for many kinds of marine life. The larvae of clams and scallops attach themselves to the leaves by means of a horny, stringlike secretion of the foot, known as a byssus thread. Algae grow on the *Zostera* leaves, and bacteria in turn are concentrated on the algae, forming a rich microscopic pasture for protozoa, isopods, copepods, waterfleas, and many other plankton organisms. Various kinds of shrimp, needlefish, pipefish, and killifish feed there too. Water movement is slowed down, and as the decay of this welter of organic material adds to the sediments brought down by the river, the water becomes increasingly shallow.

Unlike the submerged shallows, the intertidal zone with its flats of sand or mud harbors few or no plants. At their edges the ceaselessly shifting river channels by which it is traversed lay down distinct laminations with each new deposit. The mud between the channels is exposed as the tide ebbs, leaving a rippled surface upon which the inhabitants of the flats make their traces. Little mounds emerge, each with a hole in the center leading to the burrow of a worm, mollusk, or crab. The lugworm *Arenicola* (a Latin word meaning "sand dweller," though the animal actually prefers mud), is one of the most widely distributed animals of estuarine flats (Figure 38). Like its terrestrial cousin the earthworm, it betrays its presence by serpentine castings of the mud it has passed through its gut in order to extract digestible material—small, sausagelike heaps that lie at one end of the U-shaped tube in which it lives.

There are species of lugworms varying in length from three inches to a foot, all having bodies consisting of distinct segments that become smaller toward the rear end, and some being equipped with feathery gills. A lugworm feeds through a mucus-secreting proboscis which is periodically inverted so that the mud and the organic matter adhering

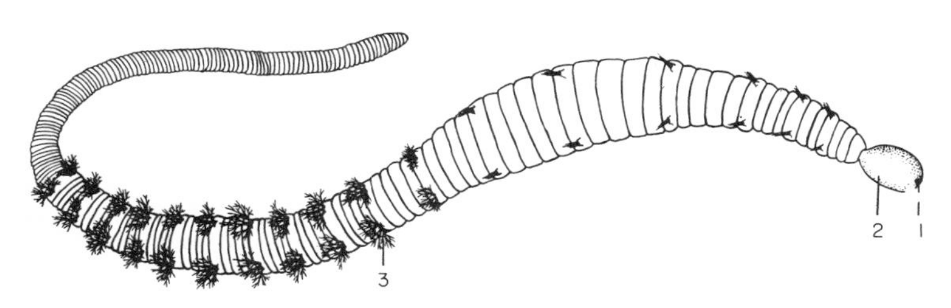

FIG. 38 The lugworm (*Arenicola*). Its segments show that it is related to the earthworm. *1.* Mouth. *2.* Proboscis. *3.* Gills. (From MacGinitie and MacGinitie, *Natural History of Marine Animals*, 1949.)

to it can be swallowed—thus efficiently excavating a burrow at the same time. Following an inherent rhythm of activity, the worm feeds only during and after high tide. During this period the proboscis is turned inside out once every five to seven minutes, and every hour or so a thorough housecleaning takes place. To accomplish this the worm creeps backward toward the exit, extrudes the feces, and flushes the tube in both head- and tailward direction by waving its gills; then it returns to its customary horizontal position in the bottom of the U.

Other tube-dwelling worms live in more sandy tidal flats, where they reinforce their burrows with a mucus secretion that hardens to a leathery consistency and thus prevents crumbling if the sand should happen to dry out temporarily. Tube-dwellers on tidal flats have many advantages; in fact, unstable as conditions may be on the surface, at even an inch below it the temperature scarcely varies, and the scourings of waves and tides have no effect. The salinity does not normally fluctuate, since water is being continually drawn in from the sea through the capillary spaces of the soil, which is flushed with fresh water only when an adjacent river channel overflows. Some tube-dwelling worms burrow down a foot or more and thus live in permanent darkness. Often they follow a rhythm shorter than the tidal cycles, one that is inherent in the animal and not triggered by events from the outside.

Near the low-tide horizon on estuarine mudflats in California, the U-shaped tubes of one of the most extraordinarily hospitable animals known are to be found. This is *Urechis caupo*, aptly called the "fat innkeeper," which sometimes harbors three or four other kinds of animals in its burrow. The innkeeper, itself often more than a foot long, pumps water through its body with peristaltic movements as a preparation for feeding, and is continuously changing its shape. Every few hours it secretes a fine-meshed net of slime at the entrance of the tube; and as water is forced through by the pumping action of the worm, microscopic food collects in the net. This remarkable process, benefiting both the innkeeper and his guests, is described as follows by the MacGinities, a husband-and-wife team of naturalists, in their book *Natural History of Marine Animals:*

Urechis goes toward one entrance of the burrow and then expands the anterior portion of its body so that the mucus glands which are situated there come in contact with the wall of the tube. The worm then begins secreting mucus, and as it continues to secrete more mucus it slowly backs down its burrow. This leaves a funnel of transparent mucus which is attached to the walls of the burrow at its upper end and to the body of the worm at its lower end, with the proboscis and the anterior portion of the body that lies beyond the mucus glands projecting into the tube. Then by a series of wave movements along its body, *Urechis* pumps a current of water through its burrow. Of necessity the water must go through the tube of mucus, which strains all the solid material from it.

When the walls of the mucus tube are clogged with small particles of food—the openings in its net are only 4/25,000,000 of an inch across—the worm ceases pumping and contracts so that the tube becomes detached from its body. It then advances again, slipping the tube over its anterior end until it can grasp it with its proboscis, and swallows it. Usually another mucus tube is spun almost as soon as the previous one has been eaten.

The innkeeper can only eat the smaller morsels of its catch; the larger ones fall to the permanent guests that share its burrow. These are most often a pea-crab, *Scleroplax*, and another, smaller worm; frequently there is also a third guest, a small fish—the goby *Clevelandia ios*—which uses the burrow chiefly for shelter. When *Urechis* is kept in an aquarium with its tube built against the glass, and is fed small morsels of clam, a fierce enmity can be observed between the crab and the second worm, the innkeeper's two chief commensals.

Clams and mussels also make use of the advantages afforded by burrowing in the mud, though they seldom dig as deeply as worms usually do. Certain bivalves likewise build reinforced tubes, whereas many others simply extend a long incurrent siphon to the surface for feeding and taking in aerated water. Besides the mollusks, which simply close their shells on becoming exposed to the air, the mudflat also has its complement of crabs, which are better adapted to an amphibious existence than either worms or mussels. Notable among these is the fiddler crab (*Uca*), which lives on the upper beaches, close to and even beyond the high-tide marks. It chooses sand with a high mud content for its burrow, whose walls thus have little tendency to cave in, and before each high tide it builds a plug of mud for the entrance. The male fiddler is sometimes brightly colored and invariably holds one claw, which is larger than the other, flexed toward the body (Figure 39). He may be

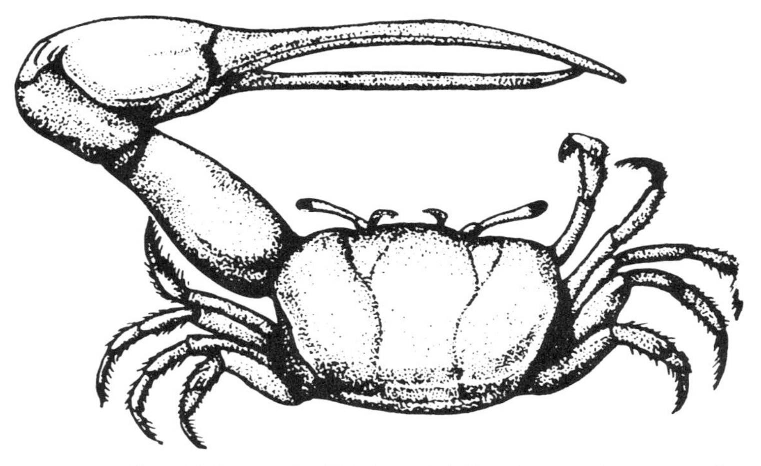

FIG. 39 The fiddler crab (*Uca*), with its claws of uneven size. (From MacGinitie and MacGinitie, 1949.)

seen sitting by his burrow, moving the large claw back and forth as if he were playing the violin. The claw is sometimes used in digging, but serves mainly as a weapon in contests with males of his own species. The two combatants lock claws and tug at each other until one relaxes his grip—perhaps losing his footing, to be thrown back over the other for a considerable distance, as in a wrestling match. At breeding time the males extend and flex their big claws, displaying them to the females. Fiddlers often go in flocks, which can be driven like cattle along the beach. Like other shore and land crabs, when cornered they will raise themselves on their legs and menacingly brandish their claws.

While the outgoing tide recedes and the still moist mudflat-dwellers tarry before retreating into their burrows, they often fall prey to shorebirds. Gulls and terns forage on mudflats in the spring; in the fall sandpipers and plovers frequent the sandier areas, and on many mudflats oystercatchers (*Hematopus*) are expert harvesters of shellfish. Birds of this, and another closely related genus (*Ostralegus*) are abundant near river mouths all over the Northern Hemisphere.

Oystercatchers are smaller than herring gulls but more conspicuously marked, with a black head, brown back, white rump, and yellow legs; the sturdy, wedge-shaped bill is brilliantly red. The hind toes have been lost in the course of evolution, and oystercatchers' tracks are therefore unmistakable, as is their loud and raucous cry. It is not known whether they open the shells of the mussels, clams, and oysters that make up a good part of their diet by cunning or by force; but they certainly rely on the bounty of the mudflats, both for their own nourishment and for that of their young that are hatched in their exposed nests, where the eggs are often left to be incubated by the sun.

Life in Estuarine Waters

High tide occurs twice daily on most shores, carrying salt water into the river mouth and retarding the flow of fresh water. On many rivers—notably the Amazon, where tidal effects can be felt 600 miles upstream—several succeeding tides may be on their way up before the first has entirely descended. Salt water is heavier than fresh water, and the salinity at the bottom of an estuary is thus usually greater than in the water at the top. As a result a river often flows into the sea over a distinct upstream wedge of ocean water, which permits bottom-dwelling marine animals to live farther upstream than those that occur near the surface.

A peculiarity of estuaries in the Northern Hemisphere is that the ocean water penetrates farther upstream on the right hand side of the river mouth, as one faces toward the land, than on the left. South of the equator the converse is true. This lopsided distribution of salt water is due to what is called Coriolis force—a displacement of all air and water currents produced by the earth's rotation. Since the descending river water and that of the incoming tide flow in opposite directions to one another, Coriolis force also diverts them in opposite directions, and fresh and salt water tend to hug opposite shores. In smaller estuaries the one-sided wedge of salt water is not very pronounced; but in Chesapeake Bay, for instance, the points on opposite shores at which the water contains identical proportions of salt may lie fifty miles apart.

The distribution of animals in estuaries is profoundly influenced by the interaction between river and sea. Clams, worms, crabs, shrimp, and other invertebrates move about very little; many of them remain in one and the same spot for their entire lives. Even among fishes, some of which make long journeys in the ocean, only a very few have evolved adaptations enabling them to go back and forth between fresh and salt water. This capability, moreover, is generally restricted to certain times in the life cycle, when the fish is physiologically ready to adjust to a drastic change in the salinity of the water that surrounds it.

The salt content of the sea is expressed in parts of salt per thousand of sea water, rather than in percentages, and in most oceans it ranges from 33 to 38 parts per thousand; the total salt content of rivers, by contrast, is usually between .065 and .3 parts per thousand. Among the many dissolved minerals in fresh and salt water, the most important are sodium, chloride, potassium, magnesium, calcium, sulfide and sulfate, and nitrate and phosphate ions; biologically they are essential for the conduction of nerve impulses, for maintaining the permeability of cells, and for the manufacture of blood corpuscles—to mention only a few of the many processes in which they play a part. The body fluids of fresh-water animals contain more, and those of many marine animals fewer, of these salts than does the water that surrounds them. Aquatic animals have permeable organs, such as the gills, which enable them to expel dissolved carbon dioxide and to take up oxygen; where these gases can enter and leave the organism, ions of minerals dissolved in the water can also diffuse through the cell walls. The permeable surfaces are kept as small as possible by such means as the shells of crabs and clams, and the scales and water-impermeable slime that cover the bodies of fishes.

A fish in a stream, for instance, normally carries in the cells enough salts, proteins, and other dissolved and suspended materials to keep the water concentration of the cell as a whole at about 70 per cent. The surrounding water, however, will have a concentration of almost 100 per cent. Inasmuch as two solutions that are separated by a permeable membrane tend to come to equilibrium, water will diffuse into the fish through the cells on the gills, and salts will tend to diffuse out. Accordingly, fresh-water animals have developed mechanisms to save them from losing vital salts, and thus from becoming diluted and eventually blowing up like a balloon attached to a water faucet. The kidneys are geared to cope with the water load; the dilute urine of a carp or a bass, for example, will be proportionally anywhere from ten to a hundred times as copious as the normal fluid elimination by man. Also, special cells on the gills and in the mouth serve to retain and even to concentrate the vital salts.

Marine fishes and other sea animals have the opposite problem: their surroundings are more salty and less watery than their own cells. The mouth and gills thus become centers of dehydration, and the fish must continually replace the water it has lost. In marine fishes a balance is maintained partly by a very scant output of highly concentrated urine, partly by taking as much water as possible from their food—where it occurs in a concentration roughly the same as in their bodies—and by drinking some sea water. This last naturally means taking up salts in the same concentration and proportion as they occur in the sea, and the salt surplus must then be eliminated. It has been found that the gills of marine fishes dispose of the excess chlorides, while other ions are retained in the gut, to be expelled with the feces.

It might at first be supposed that a salt concentration somewhere between that of the ocean and of the river—in other words, that of the brackish waters of an estuary—would be a closer approximation of the internal environment of such animals, and that they would accordingly find it easier to live there than in either fresh or salt water. But conditions in estuaries are unstable, and the wide fluctuations in salt content—as well as extreme differences in temperature that accompany tidal ebb and flow—make of the estuary a habitat more rigorous than would be encountered either upriver or out in the sea. Living in an estuary requires a versatility that is hard to reconcile with the tendency of all life processes toward a stable equilibrium.

There is one group of aquatic animals that might be expected to be less affected by salinity problems than the others—namely the whales and porpoises. Since they breathe air by coming to the surface, rather than through gills with exposed permeable membranes, they would appear to be free to go from the sea to the river and back again. Some of these mammals, notably the common porpoise (*Tursiops truncatus*) of the Florida coast, do in fact spend a part of their day in estuaries. Members of the species regularly ascend the St. Johns River, near St. Augustine, and then return to the sea several hours later when the tide recedes. However, even here the situation is not as simple as it looks;

it turns out that aquatic mammals have osmotic problems of their own.

A few years ago several porpoises from the aquarium at Marineland in Florida were transported to Silver Springs, a true fresh-water environment, where they were to be actors in a film. The location was chosen because, like most limestone springs, it has particularly clear water. The animals were in fine fettle for a day or two; but then their skins began to blister and their eyes became opaque. A biologist insisted on their being returned to sea water, where they soon recuperated. Throughout the many million years of their evolution they must presumably have become adjusted to leaving the sea only for a short while, even then perhaps not going into completely fresh water. When a porpoise stays in the river too long the corneas of its eyes become opaque and its skin becomes waterlogged. By the same token, the true fresh-water porpoises living in the rivers of Burma, China, and South America are never observed to go down to the sea, but only to travel between the river and some adjacent lakes.

The Distribution of Fishes in an Estuary

Recently two Yale University biologists completed a survey of the fishes of the Mystic River estuary in Connecticut, a typical east-coast waterway. They established a chain of collecting stations along the river mouth and out into Fisher's Island Sound. The kinds of fishes collected throughout the year illustrated the ecological and physiological principles related to the interaction between the river and the sea. The highest upriver station—to take one example—had a surface salinity of about three parts per thousand, just a little higher than that of fresh water; but at the same station the salinity of the water at a depth of six feet remained at eighteen parts per thousand, or even higher, throughout the year—clearly indicating that along the bottom a salt-water wedge or landward countercurrent to the river's flow extended far upstream. Presumably as a consequence, the rare pike taken in the survey—probably visitors from a nearby pond—were restricted to upstream surface stations, while estuarine bottom-dwellers such as the winter flounder, which could stand somewhat brackish water but not fresh, took advantage of the saline bottom waters upstream.

Likewise mummichogs and sticklebacks, also brackish-water rather than true marine species, preferred the upper and middle estuary. As collections progressed seaward, to waters where the salinity measured twenty or more parts per thousand, the numbers and kinds of fishes were greater even in winter. The total numbers were greatest in the summer, when they were dominated by such permanent residents as the winter flounder, the tomcod, and the cunner, and augmented in July and August by visitors from more southern waters. At that time the otherwise rare triggerfishes, the orange filefish, and the striped mullet were present, only to leave again when the water began to cool.

The estuary is evidently a nursery for a good many fishes, most of which lay eggs that either sink to the bottom or adhere to the pebbles or to the vegetation below the surface. It is obviously an advantage for river-mouth dwellers to have eggs that sink, since these can overwinter without danger in the relatively more saline bottom waters, which do not freeze. Nor will the eggs be affected by the spring freshets sweeping through the estuary above the landward countercurrent; here the embryos are secure until the advent of warmer weather, which simultaneously brings hatching time and the vernal plankton swarms on which the larvae can feed.

Of the fifty-odd species found in the Mystic estuary only three—the alewife, the smelt, and the eel—passed upstream into the river proper. The first two are known, as are salmon and the shad, to spend their adult lives in the sea but to spawn in fresh-water streams. Eels, on the contrary, live in rivers and lakes and return to the ocean to spawn. Their migratory habits are no less spectacular than those of the salmon; both will be dealt with in a later chapter. Upriver migrations or runs of alewife or sawbelly were familiar even to the early New England settlers, who reported that "there is a fish at New Plymouth, in April, much like the herring that comes up into the small brooks to spawn, and when the water is not even knee deep they will presse up through your hands, yea, thow you beat them with cudgels, and in such abundance as is incredible." However, the majority of fishes, and of most other marine animals, are limited in their travels by the salt content of the water; few sea animals can tolerate a salinity of less than ten parts per thousand, and few river species a salinity of more than six parts per thousand.

Oysters and Estuaries

Though the kinds of animals that can live in brackish water may be fewer than are found in the sea or even in lakes and rivers, those that have become adjusted to the estuary, with its tides and temporary dry periods, often occur in tremendous numbers. The fertile shallows of the river mouth, where the sun penetrates to the bottom, where exposure at low tide speeds up oxidation processes, and where the slowing current drops its rich muds, are the home of animals that occur by the millions—such as the famous Chesapeake blue crabs, the bay scallops, and above all the oysters.

A mussel can slowly creep with its foot, and a scallop can swim by the recoil of its flapping valves; but their relative the oyster has to stay put wherever its spat falls. Some species need a firmer bottom than others, but they all thrive in the rich plankton pastures of a typical temperate estuary. Long Island Sound, Chesapeake Bay, and the sandy coasts of western France with their river mouths are—or were—among the prime oyster grounds of the world.

Oysters and other estuarine mollusks were among the earliest foods of man. On the coasts of all continents kitchen

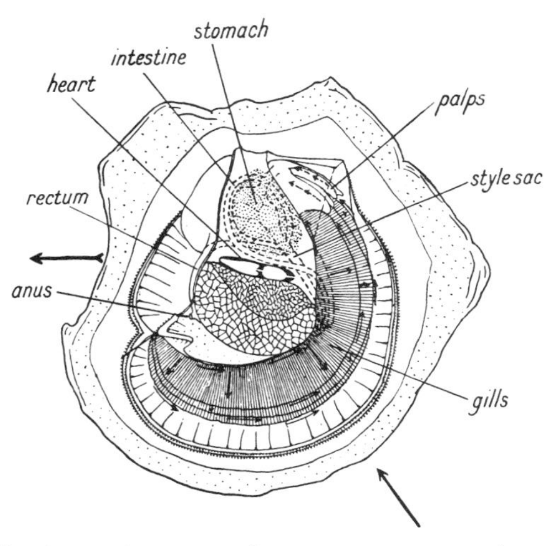

FIG. 40 The internal organs of an oyster as seen after removal of one valve. (From Yonge, *Oysters*, 1960.)

middens—as ancient shell heaps are called by anthropologists—testify that primitive man may have gathered wild oysters even before he learned the arts of hunting and fishing. Today oyster farming in estuarine waters is a food-raising endeavor no less intensive, and often both more profitable and more productive, than any on dry land.

The oyster, like many other mollusks, is a filter feeder. Opening an oyster (Figure 40), by cutting the muscle that keeps the shells closed, exposes a visceral mass consisting of the heart, a greenish-brown stomach whose attachments are often wrongly referred to as the liver, a semicircular fringe of comblike gills, and on the outside the whitish mantle, bordering the nacreous inner shell surface. On opposite sides are the incurrent and exhalant siphons that carry water through the organism. Food consisting of minute diatoms and other microorganisms sticks to the mucus on the gills and is propelled toward the mouth by rows of beating cilia. These also create the current through the shell and past the feeding surfaces, thus allowing eight or ten gallons of water an hour to pass through the perforated, sievelike gills. The cilia beat in a complicated rhythm as they concentrate and propel the food toward the mouth; through a microscope they resemble a field of tall grass, bending and rising in waves as though driven by the wind.

During the course of evolution it is believed that the ancestors of the oyster once moved about, since its larva today retains a foot. The oyster also apparently had eyes, for eye spots are still present on the larva. Now the adult retains only a mechanical and chemical sense to inform it of changes in its environment. An increase in the sediment load, for instance, is immediately countered by more frequent and rapid movements of the shells, thus creating a strong current which flushes the gills of accumulated irritants.

In one of the several pockets in its stomach, the oyster has an organ unique in the animal kingdom. It consists of a rod of stiff mucus, called the crystalline style, that is rotated by cilia and contains starch- and cellulose-digesting enzymes. Food is mixed by rotation and is dissolved as it advances into the stomach. It is continuously re-formed at its other tip, to reconstitute what was lost in digestion. The style is chiefly notable in being the only continuously turning structure in the animal kingdom—the closest approach to a camshaft or a wheel mechanism to be found anywhere in nature.

To compensate for not being able to move about, the

oyster produces a hundred million or more eggs and an even greater number of sperm cells. It can also change sex: some specimens of the European oyster have been known to have been twice female and once male during the same breeding season. Oysters spawn throughout the summer; and when the days are long and the water is warm, larvae appear peri-

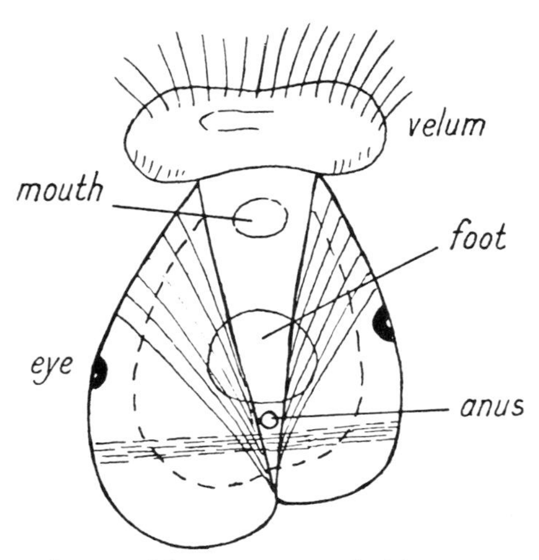

FIG. 41 Oyster larva, with eye spots and ciliary crown for swimming. (From Yonge, 1960.)

odically in consonance with tidal stages and the phases of the moon. Some oysters, including the European species, retain their eggs within the gill cavity, where they are fertilized by sperm in the incurrent stream; others, among them the American oyster (*Crassostrea virginica*), expel both eggs and sperm into the water.

Whether free-floating or temporarily retained inside the shell, the larvae soon appear in the plankton. Each one has about the mouth a large ring of cilia which enable it to swim, and besides the larval eyes (Figure 41) it has a pair of sense organs—the statocysts—for responding to gravity and maintaining balance. These organs are entirely lost while the other embryonic structures become transformed into those of the adult. About twenty days after spawning the young oyster, or spat, is ready to attach itself. It then sinks until it encounters a solid object, which may be the shell of another oyster, and which it explores with its foot. If the object is found suitable, the oyster empties a special gland containing the byssal cement—a sticky substance that glues it to the substrate for the rest of its life. The ideal surface for a successful spatfall, as the process of settling is called, will be clean but not too clean. Oysters grow most successfully if they settle on a growth of bacteria and sessile diatoms, near small hydroid animals and also near other larvae.

Experiments in which the soft parts of recently attached larvae were destroyed with a hot needle, leaving the shells intact, showed that far fewer larvae settled where there were dead rather than living members of their own species. Chemical clues are believed to lead to a bunching of animals that are tied to one place by their life habits. The same gregariousness that is found in oysters also occurs in other sessile animals, including barnacles and small tube-forming worms. There can be no doubt that it ensures successful reproduction by bringing together many males and females of the species.

The oyster's habits make it an ideal animal to cultivate. A successful oyster farmer must own or lease a piece of estuarine bottom where salinity and fertility favor the growth of oysters. He has to give the larvae good places for attachment—tiles, old oyster shells, lime-sprayed egg crates, and the like. Presently these objects are raised and the young oysters are collected and transplanted, less densely, to new grounds, simply by broadcasting them from a boat. They may stay there to mature, or they may be thinned out once more and transplanted again before they are finally harvested. The equipment for the latter operation consists of a boat with ample deck space, a dredge, perhaps a winch, and tongs for use in shallower water.

Few possible methods of oyster cultivation have been left untried. The Romans grew oysters on stakes and used trays suspended from slats or ropes to catch the spat. In Europe the practice of throwing in old empty shells as "cultch"—a collective name for the materials on which the spat can attach itself—has been followed since Saxon times. In the Far East it was long the custom to place bamboo fences in inlets; when the oysters had settled on them these fences were removed, set upright on dry land, and raked to collect the young oysters, which were then transferred to appropriate submerged growing grounds. Nowadays the Japanese collect oyster spat on shells suspended from rafts and other devices, thus using not only the sea bottom but also the water above it as the oyster's growing space, and incidentally reducing the incidence of such crawling enemies as starfishes and oyster drills.

Algae cultures, which can now be automatically maintained and illuminated day and night, provide food for the young oysters, which will have been reared in hatcheries from carefully nurtured parents, selected for fast growth, high fat and glycogen production, and resistance to certain diseases. The oyster is well on the way of becoming another domesticated animal—the first mollusk to join this category along with cats, dogs, cows, sheep, carp, and bees.

Perhaps no discussion of oysters should omit a reference to the popular belief that they should be eaten only during the months whose names contain the letter *r*. Fresh oysters can be eaten at any time, though it is true that they are leaner and less sweet in the *r*-less months of the summer, their spawning time. Oysters are at their best in the fall and the early spring, when their food goes into the storage of fat and glycogen, rather than into making eggs and sperm. The chief reason for the month-without-*r* rule, however, is that although oysters spoil easily at any time, they do so most easily in the summer; the interdiction against eating them then harks back to a time when refrigeration was less well developed than it is today.

Salt Marshes

The mudflats between low and high tide levels are usually barren of conspicuous vegetation, though mats of algae may cover the ground in protected places. Toward the high-tide level the hardiest plants begin to colonize the beach. These seaward pioneers of the salt marsh must be very tolerant of salt, and since it is difficult for seed plants to grow in salty soil—let alone temporarily submerged in salt water—only a few plants have made the adjustment. In the Northern Hemisphere the most widespread are those belonging to the genus *Spartina*, which in New England are collectively called "thatch." Belts of thatch usually start with a few straggling plants on the low sandy flats that have emerged from the estuary as a result of tidal and current action.

The grass spreads, more often by underground runners than by seeding, until in a few years a grassy island has emerged from the sand. Miniature dams, pools, and smaller islets appear in this larger island, which as the intervening channels are filled in eventually becomes linked to the mainland. The water still covers the grass at high tide; but as the debris and sediments it carries are trapped, the land becomes higher and drier. The rise in sea level after the last glaciation caused the low-tide level to move progressively inland, accumulating new sand year by year and thus leading to the emergence of higher and higher salt marshes. As the profuse root systems of succeeding layers of thatch became buried, air was excluded from them and the submerged remains of thatchgrass were turned into beds of peat, which in places are more than twenty feet deep.

Where only the highest spring tides can flood the marsh, the thatchgrass itself will produce conditions unfavorable for its own further spread, and plants less tolerant of salt and with somewhat lesser needs of moisture—such as rushes (*Juncus*) and panicgrass (*Panicum*)—will take over. Even asters and goldenrod can grow in the transition to the high marsh, which will then give way to low shrubs, alder, willow, and finally, farther inland, to spruce, oak, or maple.

Deltas

Where the river's encounter with the sea produces a delta, the transition zone differs notably from the mudflats and salt marshes of a tidal estuary. It was once believed that deltas could form only where the tides were weak—a supposition which has since been disproved by the measurement of the tides in such rivers as the Ganges, the Colorado, and the Amazon, which end in deltas despite spring tides with a height of fifteen feet or more. On the other hand, the relatively slight tidal action of the Mediterranean Sea has no doubt contributed to the building of deltas by such rivers as the Rhone, the Ebro, the Guadalquivir, and—most famous of all—the Nile, to which the name of the formation was first assigned. Below Cairo its channel diverges into the Damietta arm on the east and the Rosetta arm on the west, thus forming a triangle whose shortest side is bounded by the coast and which consists of a lowland region intersected by smaller streams, lakes, and canals. The shape of the area suggests that of the Greek capital letter *delta* (Δ), whence its name.

Where the action of waves and current is mild and where the river carries much sediment, new land can build up rapidly. A notable example is the delta of the river Po in the Adriatic Sea, which has been observed for almost twenty-five hundred years. In the sixth century B.C. a Greek seaport was located at Adria, twenty-five miles from the present mouth as the crow flies; in A.D. 69 a canal had to be built to reach the port, which soon afterward ceased to function. During the Renaissance the waters of the Po began to be regulated by dykes, which helped the river to carry into the sea the material that would formerly have been deposited over the valley floor. From then on the delta grew even faster; at present the mouth of the river's main branch, the Po della Pila, is moving eastward at a rate of 400 feet a year. But as rivers go, the Po is only medium-sized; the lowlands arising from the sea at its mouth are measured in acres, as against the many square miles that have been built up by the Amazon or the Mississippi (Figure 42).

The amount of suspended material carried by the river is, of course, what determines how fast its delta grows. Of the billions of tons a year of silt, mud, and finer colloidal matter brought into the oceans by all the rivers of the world, the Mississippi alone transports over 700 million tons past New Orleans and into the Gulf of Mexico. The finest particles are carried out far into the sea—river water can be detected by its color as far as 200 miles from the Gulf Coast, while the heavier material, dropped closer by, is being added to the delta.

In the slow-flowing arms of the delta where the water is fresh and the effects of the tides are hardly noticeable, silt and organic colloids dropped by the river become a growing medium for algae and diatoms, which decay to form an underwater soil favorable for the growth of rooted aquatic plants. Pondweeds with trailing frondlike leaves, or water milfoil (*Myriophyllum*) and coontail (*Ceratophyllum*) then begin to fill the canals. These plants, still submerged and variously adapted to flowing water, in turn inevitably

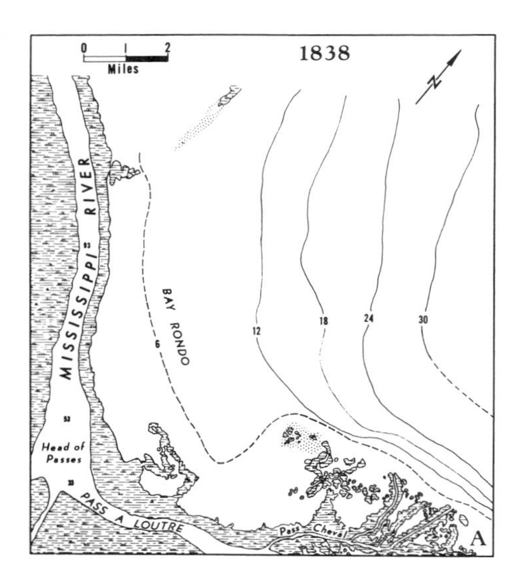

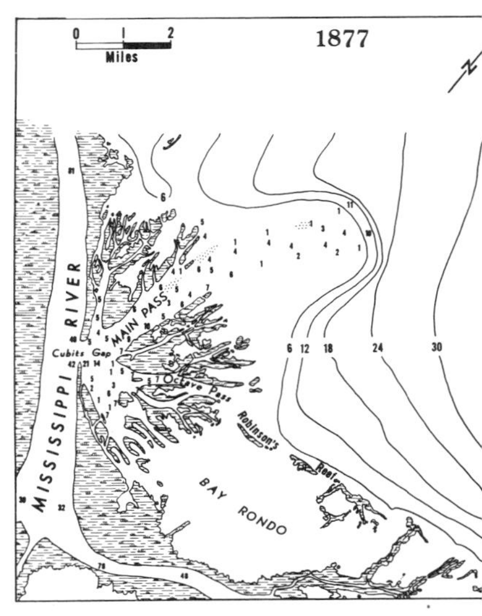

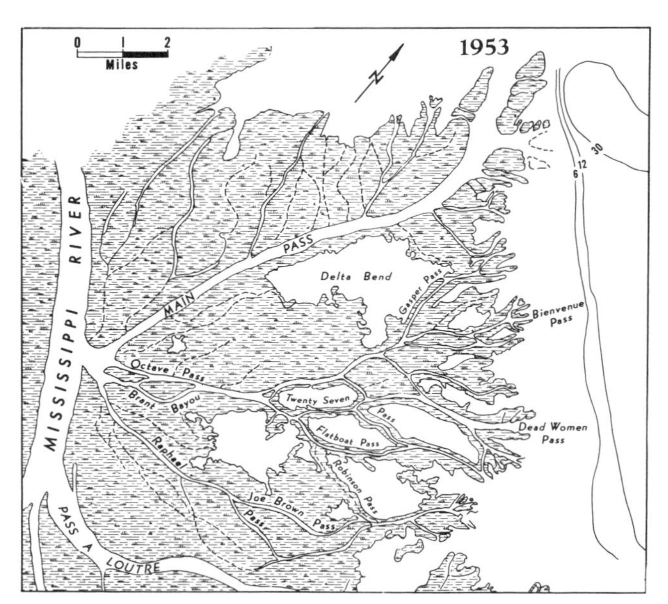

FIG. 42 Formation of Mainpass area on Mississippi Delta between 1838 and 1953. From U.S. Army Corps of Engineers.

slow down the currents and trap sediments among the whorls of leaves on their stems.

Farther inland, the next step toward the building of dry land is taken by emergent plants, first by bulrushes (*Scirpus*) and cattails (*Typha*), and then where the water is only a foot or two deep by arrowheads (*Sagittaria*), but above all by the reed-grasses (*Phragmites*), which correspond to the rush and panicgrass stage of the salt marsh. Though the marsh may still be inundated for part of the year, the decaying plant remains increasingly exclude the water. Soon an alder or a willow can take root, and the new land has become consolidated; now only a violent flood will break it down again.

Mangroves and Mudskippers

The waterways of a delta are often difficult or even impossible to penetrate. Channels clogged with bulrushes frequently turn into blind alleys; in the cypress swamps the knees of cypress trees, the many creepers underfoot, and the feathery shrouds of Spanish moss overhead combine to obstruct both the passage and the view. But the most impenetrable of all delta thickets are undoubtedly the mangrove swamps that choke the mouths of tropical rivers. They accumulate mud so rapidly that in India before the nineteenth century they prevented the maintenance of usable ports. It was only when steam-powered dredges became available that man could keep up with the mangroves in the delta of the Ganges.

Mangrove thickets are made up of plants that settle out river sediments both by obstructing the flow and by chemical precipitation of the colloids in the water. The former action is best observed on the seaward side of the mangrove belt. There one finds a profuse development of aerial roots that may either grow straight up, looking like giant asparagus tips, or take the form of snakelike creepers, or send out whorls of prop-roots that arise high on the stem and then arch downward into the mud. The undergrowth in a dense mangrove swamp appears to be composed of innumerable gigantic petrified spiders. The prop-roots are dotted with pores, through which they absorb air needed by the lower portion of the plant, since the mud in which they grow is almost entirely devoid of oxygen.

The extensive development of the mangroves' elevated roots slows down both river and tidal currents and retains the sediments they carry. The thickets spread all the more rapidly not only because new plants arise quickly from the spreading roots, but also because there are "live-bearing" mangroves as well. The seeds of the latter germinate while they are still on the trees, where even the ripening fruit may grow a root from one to three feet long before dropping. Such immediate holdfasts allow the seedlings to grow into young trees within a very short time. If the seeds drop from the trees at high water, they may be stranded downstream, where they are able to take root more rapidly than other plants which do not come with their roots already formed.

The chemical action comes into play in the landward stands; here many mangroves have their leaves covered with salt crystals, exuded by special glands whose function is to concentrate and give off salts. For in spite of being located near fresh water, the soil in which the mangroves are rooted has an extraordinarily high salt content, at least for part of the year. It may be exposed to the air for weeks, especially at neap tides during the dry season, when the only moisture to reach it will be the sea water that seeps in from below, to evaporate almost immediately as it comes to the surface. As a result the concentration of chlorides in the soil around the mangrove roots may be as high as 80 or even 120 parts per thousand, as compared with the 19 parts per thousand in ordinary sea water. After the roots have absorbed the salts, the transpiration stream conveys them to the leaves, where they form a white crust.

When the rivers rise after the monsoon rains have begun to fall, the soil surrounding the mangroves is inundated with muddy water, carrying a heavy load of silt and colloids. The rain washes the salt from the leaves into the water below, where the increased salinity causes the colloids to coagulate and the mud to settle out more rapidly than would happen in fresh water. The mangrove belt thus builds up both toward the river and toward the sea.

The mangrove stands of a tropical delta are traversed by many natural canals, and there may be some exposed mudflats, especially at low tide. At the edge of these flats lives the mudskipper (*Periophthalmus*), a remarkable animal peculiar to this habitat. A small fish whose length rarely exceeds seven inches, it is brown with iridescent markings of silver and blue on its sides and on its divided dorsal fin. Its eyes are set on the top of its head and can be elevated in the manner of a small periscope, as well as lowered under regular eyelids so as to be flush with the surface. The mudskipper is as much at home in and on the mud as it is in the water, since it is able to stay out in the air for hours at a time.

Catching one of these little fish is surprisingly difficult because they move with agility even on ground somewhat drier than the semiliquid mud. It is sometimes possible to capture a few with a long-handled butterfly net, but only at the risk of falling headlong and emerging caked with mud from head to toe. The mudskipper has pectoral fins with long muscular bases, more like arms than fins and which are moved in unison like oars. Its trail in the mud consists of three streaks: one in the center, made by the body, and two lateral ones by the moving fins.

Mudskippers can also jump, and may be seen perched on the aerial roots of the mangroves, a foot or more off the ground. From this vantage point they scan the surroundings with eyes moving independently, alert to the slightest movement around them, waiting for a crab or another small animal to emerge from its burrow. When frightened they rush to their hiding places, holes in the mud between the low and high tide marks. Each hole is surrounded by a miniature moat and enclosed by a rampart made of mud. When the tide goes out, water remains in the pool, and the fish may sit astride the wall before coming out onto the mudflat to hunt for its prey. The rampart and the burrow are of firmer consistency than the surrounding mud, since the fish builds them from stiffer material brought up with its mouth, pellet by pellet, from below the surface.

The mudskipper's eyes are so constructed that it can see equally well in air and in water, and from beneath the surface it can make out what is going on outside the pool. Its retina is well supplied with cone cells like those of the human eye, and it is, therefore, believed to have keen color vision. Behaving as it does in this most unfishlike manner, it has had to solve the problem of taking oxygen both from the air and from the water. On examination the top of the mudskipper's head, which is so often held above the surface of the water, it turns out to be richly supplied with capillaries and to be capable of functioning as an accessory air-breathing organ. The main air-breathing tissues lie inside the mouth, on its first two gills; the other two gill arches bear gill lamellae, used for aquatic respiration like those of any other fish.

There are other air-breathing fishes, some of which must even come to the surface to exchange waste carbon dioxide for fresh oxygen; but none of these is capable of taking a siesta on mangrove roots out in the air. The tolerance of the mudskipper for drier surroundings than fishes usually frequent has been tested by biologists. After being treated with thyroid extract, they stayed out of the water much longer and more frequently than the untreated controls, and the air-breathing tissues inside their mouths increased in size. Their reaction to thyroid hormones is remarkable in itself, but becomes still more significant when it is noted that tadpoles injected with thyroid extract have reacted in an analogous way, transforming into frogs prematurely, losing their gills, and acquiring lungs—thus revealing what may have been one of the mechanisms involved in the emergence of primitive vertebrates from the sea to a permanent terrestrial existence.

6

Rivers and Animal Migrations

At certain seasons the marshes of the Mississippi delta, and of other river mouths in the same region, are alive with birds. Many of the shore and water birds that nest among the Thelon waterways spend the winter on the Gulf Coast. Others—the plovers, for instance—migrate south of the equator, but even they pause in the delta marshes for a while en route to and from the north. In the spring, just before the big trek begins, the waters of the delta fairly swarm with birds continually rising, alighting, and rising again.

At that time, an explorer taking a canoe through the waterways and shallow lakes of the marsh looks upward through a fringe of bright green rushes at the many flying forms in the sky. Around him huge lily pads border the patches of open water, and here and there a white or purple blossom emerges. Algae, water mosses, and floating ferns are so dense as to give an illusion that the boat is supported by plants, which can be heard gently scraping against its side whenever there is a lull in the myriad cries of the birds overhead.

Flocks of ducks rest on the lakes; often there are five or six kinds mingling together, splashing and feeding. A few loons keep a lofty distance, frequently disappearing for long dives, using their wings as underwater flippers, and overtaking fish with ease. A grebe or two also floats low in the water, alertly turning its head on a gracefully curved neck. Grebes (Colymbidae) and loons (Gaviidae) are more closely related to their ancestors the reptiles than any other group of birds now found in North America. They are also the most aquatic of North American birds, and derive their food entirely from the water. The young begin to swim almost immediately after hatching, and the feet of the adults are so entirely adapted to paddling that they are exceedingly clumsy on land: the tibia or drumstick is actually buried beneath the skin, so that the heel is located almost at the rear of the body. To enhance their swimming ability still further, the large toes of loons and grebes are either webbed or broadly lobed.

Grebes and loons have an uncanny way of disappearing below the water's surface; often they do not tip up to dive as ducks do, but merely sink like a submarine. They often puzzle hunters who want to follow them and who count on a bird's needing to come up for air; a hunter who cannot detect the bird anywhere near where he counted on its surfacing will swear that it has drowned itself. It is true that grebes can stay under water longer than many other birds, but their seemingly miraculous disappearance is accounted for by their habit of diving toward shore and then slipping in among the reeds, where, with only the bill and a part of the head projecting above the water, they remain motionless until the danger is past, simply breathing and observing their surroundings.

The explorer of the delta may eventually abandon his

canoe, to wade through a few inches of water onto the springy ground, which is the domain of the marsh-dwellers, as distinguished from the true water birds. In Louisiana the marshes may be bordered by willows or by cypress trees; in other deltas—such as that of the Nile, where many European birds spend the winter—the marshes are bordered by dykes fringed with stands of mimosa and date palms. Some marsh birds, notably ibises and egrets, stand out from afar as white dots against the green background of a sedge meadow or the trees that are their roosting places.

Egrets often feed in flocks, stepping slowly and gingerly on their stilted legs, toes folding as the foot is lifted and spreading again for more secure footing as it comes down. The head is bent as the bird scans the ground with small jerky movements, the strong bill pointed downward at an angle, now and then seizing an insect, a lizard, or a frog. Less conspicuous relatives of the egrets are the herons, the cranes, the rails, and the bitterns. They do not rely as much as their showier relatives on being in flocks for protection, but make use of their protective coloration. Yet they are wary of intruders, even on the wintering grounds where they have no brood to protect.

The bitterns, the smallest members of the heron family, are the genii of the marsh—shy, alert, and adept at concealment. Their undersides and their long necks are vertically striped or freckled with brown and white. When disturbed they "freeze," pointing their beaks into the air, rather than take wing (Figure 43). While they remain motionless the dark freckles or streaks on their breasts blend so well with the shadows among the stems of the marsh plants that they are perfectly camouflaged. The eyes are set low on the head and close to the beak, so that the bird can see ahead even when its head is pointed skyward. The larger herons, besides feeding on all sorts of aquatic life, occasionally stray to upland hillsides and cultivated fields, where they hunt

FIG. 43 Nest of a bittern. Both young and old birds "freeze" with their heads pointing upward so as to blend into the vertical pattern of light and shade of the marsh plants. Photo from Michigan Department of Conservation.

for small mammals ranging in size from mice to pocket gophers. Solitary and wary and keen of eyesight, they fly away as soon as they spot a man at field-glass range.

Herons (Ardeidae) are often confused with cranes (Gruidae); however, although both are marsh or wetland birds and both migrate, there are some notable differences between the two. Herons nest in trees, cranes on the ground; herons fly with their necks folded close to the body in an S-curve, cranes with their necks and heads extended. Herons are meat-eaters exclusively, whereas cranes not only take almost any living animal food from the water but also feed on vegetable matter, such as corn, in addition to spearing insects, frogs, lizards, snakes, or mice in meadows and uplands. Neither herons nor cranes have exactly melodious voices; but those of the latter are by far the louder and more resonant.

The sandhill crane (*Grus canadensis*), the only large member of its family now common in America, has a coiled windpipe that lengthens as the bird matures, until it extends into the keel of the breastbone. As a result its voice has remarkable carrying power, and may be heard for a long time after the bird itself has disappeared from view. The even larger and very conspicuous whooping crane (*Grus americana*) is now almost extinct, mainly because its species lost out in the competition with early white settlers for the best river lowlands and prairie marshes, most of which were drained. Whooping cranes stand from four to five feet tall and are mostly white, with black primaries and wing coverts and a bare patch of carmine-red on the head. The ornithologist Thomas Nuttall wrote in 1811 of their deafening clangor as they passed high in the air on their northward migrations through the Mississippi Valley.

River Flyways

Bird migration, one of the most mysterious and spectacular patterns of animal behavior, has filled man with wonder from very early times. The first attempts to explain it now seem naïve and superstitious: cuckoos, for example, were believed to turn into hawks in winter, and swallows were thought to hibernate in the mud—an understandable misconception, since swallows often gather in the marshes in great numbers before they leave for the south. It was only with the scientific banding of birds, begun during the last century, that the long seasonal flights of birds were verified. From hundreds of thousands of individual banding records it is now clear that many birds regularly follow prominent landmarks on their northward and southward migrations. The major routes in North America appear to be the Atlantic and Pacific shorelines, the eastern margin of the Rocky Mountain chain, and perhaps most important of all, the Missouri and Mississippi rivers. In Europe the silver arteries of the Rhine and the Rhone, and in Africa that of the Nile, make up the route followed by a majority of the birds migrating between the two continents.

However, not all migrating birds follow such obvious landmarks. An arctic tern, for instance, upon leaving its northern nesting grounds along the Thelon or even farther to the north, will normally veer southeastward to fly across the Atlantic, skirting the coast of Africa, passing the Cape of Good Hope, and finally wintering in the Antarctic. A curlew that spends its summers in Alaska normally flies to Polynesia for the winter—a journey of 20,000 miles, nearly all over open water, without any obvious direction-giving landmarks below.

There is now good evidence that animals have a sense of time, a built-in "clock" set by the cycle of light and darkness. The precise duration of night and day will differ in different parts of the globe; and like man, the most incessant traveler, birds and other animals have an innate time sense that can be readjusted to nights and days of different lengths. It has thus been inferred that birds possess the instinctive equivalent of a chronometer for navigating with the sun or the stars as reference points. Such navigation is presumed to rely on the arc the sun describes in the sky during the day, reaching its highest elevation at midday. The angle between the plane of the arc and the horizon increases as one travels south in the Northern Hemisphere, and vice versa. Similarly, as one travels from east to west along a meridian—the point at which the sun reaches its zenith, or the hour of noon—will occur progressively later. One can learn to trace in one's mind the daily arc of the sun —especially its position at noon—and thus acquire a built-in chronometer. Thus by comparing, as one travels, the position of the sun at a particular time with the position it had in the home sky, it should be possible to tell in what direction one is traveling. Birds have been shown to be capable of learning even more difficult tasks; it follows, therefore, that a bird flying in a southeasterly direction, for instance, may detect that the sun is climbing higher and reaching the zenith a few minutes earlier than at the point of its departure; this perception may serve to determine its course. In the same manner, the stars differ in their relative positions in the night sky at different latitudes; they could thus, at least theoretically, serve as direction indicators to migrating birds.

Several biologists have criticized the sun-navigation theory of bird migration on the basis of the "complex calculations" required of birds; others have argued that the change in arc due to a day's travel northward or southward is so slight as to be beyond the animal's sensory capacity. It must not be forgotten that the acuity of human eyes and ears can be improved by training to exceed their everyday performance and that many birds have about the same threshold of visual acuity as man. Helmut Adler of the American Museum of Natural History who has tested the vision of some migrating birds and examined pertinent experiments of many other scientists has this to say on the subject: ". . .

it can be pointed out that present theories of a complete system of navigation seem to make excessive demands on the sense capacities of animals. On the other hand it appears probable that celestial clues may be utilized in direction finding, where the possibility of correction of course exists and where landmarks and visual search may be used to compensate for errors introduced by sensory limitations."

In spite of Adler's caution recent experiments strongly suggest that birds do indeed find their way by the position of the sun in the sky. Numbers of captured adult birds were transferred just before migration time, some to the east, some to the west along the meridian of their summer residence, whereupon they flew respectively southwest and southeast, aiming toward their customary flyway and compensating for their displacement by navigation; as a result a majority sooner or later found their old flyway. However, young birds that had never been south, when subjected to a similar experiment, flew exactly in the direction they would have taken had they departed from home—the obvious inference being that they had only a general sense of the direction in which they ought to fly. Young birds reared in captivity without ever seeing the sun, and released under a moonlit sky at the time of migration, have oriented themselves to the moon. These and other observations suggest that the light source in the sky has strong biological significance for migrating birds.

Another kind of experiment was performed in the laboratory by Gustav Kraemer, a young German biologist, who had noticed that migratory birds kept in cages would make short attempts at flight at the time when wild members of their species were about to leave for the winter. The movements in the cage were aimed roughly in the direction of the migration route. When Kraemer excluded the sun and the portion of the sky near it from the bird's view, no such "intention movements" occurred. By reflecting the sun and adjacent sky into the cages from carefully placed mirrors, he could make it appear to occupy a different place in the sky. A displacement of the sun's arc by 90° led the birds to follow suit; wherever it appeared, the reflected sun was still the source from which they took their cues of direction.

Although birds are apparently capable of rough navigation by the sun and possibly by the stars, rivers are still very important, as Adler suggests. Birds have been observed to follow the windings of a watercourse even when they have had a view broad enough to permit taking a shortcut. For instance, turkey vultures flying across the Isthmus of Panama where the canal takes a zigzag pattern are certainly able to take in much of its course at a glance; nevertheless they follow every turning in the waterway. Even the largest birds rarely migrate at altitudes of more than three thousand feet, and smaller birds generally travel at no more than a few hundred feet—another indication of the importance of landmarks.

Rivers not only offer a clear landmark for birds to follow, but also afford places where they can find shelter and food. This is an especially important advantage for some water and shore birds that migrate north so early that they might not find open water on lakes, and must likewise rely on the plants and small animals that emerge first along the shores of streams and rivers. The profusion of seeds in the river lowlands in the fall, and the stubblefields that have existed since man occupied the river valley, offer another incentive for following the river.

Geese in particular make use of the stubblefields, where flocks descend as night falls, with sentinels posted so that the rest can feed before they settle down to sleep. At daybreak they feed once more before continuing their flight; and on the following evening another flock will almost surely descend on the same field. Some groups may stay for a few days in a particularly rich spot; when a new flock chooses the same field from the air they will circle several times, giving voice to their indignation at finding it occupied, while those on the ground reply that they were there first.

This pattern of resting, moving on, and resting again explains why the over-all speed of bird travel is moderate. On overland routes few birds exceed thirty miles a day on their spring advance, though they fly much faster over the ocean. The Gulf of Mexico, for instance, is traversed in one lap, with an extended rest before and after the ocean flight.

Two theories have been proposed to explain how and why birds developed their migratory habit. One, the so-called Southern Home Theory, assumes that birds originally evolved in their tropical winter homes, where they multiplied profusely and became overcrowded, and that at the end of the last glacial period they spread into new territories to raise their broods. The theory reckons with a short time span, as organic evolution goes, since the northern glaciers vanished from the birds' present breeding grounds only ten or twelve thousand years ago. However, its proponents cite in defense of their hypothesis the number of species like the orchard oriole, which leaves its breeding grounds in July and goes south long before the approach of winter. On the other hand, the more plausible Northern Home Theory assumes that long before the ice age a subtropical Northern Hemisphere swarmed with nonmigratory bird life. Millions of years ago the climate began to cool, and as the winters gradually became more severe the birds had to move or perish. Supposedly migrations covered only short distances at first, but when the large continental glaciers had formed, the birds were presumably forced to remain continuously close to their present wintering grounds. Since the glaciers have advanced and retreated at least five times during the last million years, the birds' migratory habit would have been reinforced each time the northland was opened up again by the retreat of the ice, thus freeing niches for raising fledglings, with long summer days and an abundance of seeds and insects.

The Travels of the Salmon

Migratory birds follow rivers simply as convenient landmarks on their routes, and straying from the water does not necessarily mean losing their way. It is naturally otherwise with migratory fishes. Some of these, notably the eel, live in fresh water for most of their lives and spawn in the sea; others spend most of their lives in the sea but enter freshwater streams to spawn. Among the latter, the anadromous* fishes, the various species of salmon are the most spectacular, as well as the best known and economically the most important. They occur everywhere in the temperate Northern Hemisphere; some spawn near estuaries, but most species lay their eggs in the cold upper reaches or headwaters of certain river systems.

One of these, the Atlantic salmon (*Salmo salar*), occurs in Europe from the Bay of Biscay to Norway, and in America from Maine to northern Quebec and Newfoundland. When traveling upstream, *salar* leaps upward over falls with a height of ten feet or more, providing the water below has the proper conditions for a takeoff. The Atlantic salmon will return to spawn twice or, rarely, three times. His Pacific relatives of the genus *Oncorhynchus*, however, spawn only once and then die. Their name (from the Greek words *onkos*, meaning "bulk" or "mass," and *rhynchos*, "snout"), refers to the large hooked beak grown by the male salmon at spawning time (Figure 44). The Pacific salmon species are the sockeye (*O. nerka*), the pink (*O.*

* A word from the Greek *ana*, "upwards," and *dromein*, "to wander."

gorbuscha), the chum (*O. keta*), the coho (*O. kisutch*), and the chinook or king salmon (*O. tshawytscha*), which may reach a weight of one hundred pounds. All live in the north Pacific and spawn in the rivers of Asia as well as America. One or two other species of *Oncorhynchus* occur

FIG. 44 Pink salmon (*Oncorhynchus gorbuscha*) at spawning time. *Above*, head of the male showing hooked snout; *below*, head of the female. (From Lagler, Bardach, and Miller, *Ichthyology*, 1962.)

only on the Asian side. The specific names of the various Pacific salmons are derived not from the Greek but from the Indian languages of the Pacific Northwest and also from the Russian. Indian middens on the Klamath River dating from pre-Columbian days are full of salmon bones; and even today, since salmon remains one of their staple foods, Indians have a legal right to fish for it at any time of the year, without regard for government regulations. The Russian influence, also noticeable in old place-names in Alaska, is a reminder that the forty-ninth state, which was once called Russian-America, owes much of its early development to Russians who went there by way of Asia before the early American pioneers had crossed their own continent.

The flavor even of canned salmon is certainly one reason why among American fishery products the salmon is second only to the shrimp in commercial importance. Another reason is its migratory spawning habit. The more uniform in size and the more concentrated in location a fish species is, the easier it is to develop highly mechanized and efficient catching and processing methods. The herring, with their schooling habit, and the salmon, with their regular journeys upstream, are both good cases in point. From spring to fall, one by one the species of Pacific salmon appear in thousands at the mouths of their ancestral rivers on their way to their particular spawning grounds; and as a result their capture is relatively easy. A high-seas fishery is being developed by the Japanese—thus adding greatly to the already complex problems of salmon conservation, since the Asian and American stocks of Pacific salmon mix in the center of the north Pacific.

It is not known whether the salmon originally developed in fresh water and only later invaded the marine habitat for a part of their lives, or whether they were salt-water fishes that became adapted to the transition to and from a fresh-water environment. Both theories have their defenders; but a compromise theory that makes more sense places the cradle of the salmonid fishes (salmon, trout, and whitefish) in the cold coastal waters of the Northern Hemisphere during the glacial period. According to the theory, much precipitation and intermittent melting rendered these areas less saline then than they are now; spawning may then have taken place in streams very close to the coast, and as the migratory habit developed and as inland waters became accessible, the original stock evolved into separate species.

In view of the difficulty aquatic animals have in crossing the physiological barrier between the sea and fresh water, it is not surprising to find that the migrating salmon can go to and from the sea only at certain stages in its life history. Young salmon—or parr and smolt, as they are called at successive stages—undergo changes in their physiology that predispose them to swim downstream or to let themselves be carried by the current. At that time their body shading changes from the vertical patches of dark and light that protect them in the varied light conditions in the river to blue-black above and silvery white below—a shading typical of high-seas fishes and an outward sign of the internal changes that are fitting them for the exigencies of ocean life.

Although many books and articles have been published on the causes and mechanics of these changes, much about them remains unknown. It is clear, at any rate, that the downstream journeys of migrating salmon begin in the spring when the days grow longer and the water becomes warmer. Both these seasonal changes, but especially the first, cause an increase in the activity of the pituitary gland. The pituitary, in fishes as in all other vertebrates, is the master gland of internal secretion, producing hormones that govern the activity of the thyroid and adrenal glands and of the reproductive organs. When a young salmon is ready to migrate its thyroid gland becomes very active, and the rate of its metabolism rises. It swims around and begins to move downstream. That the juvenile fish invariably goes down- and not upstream must be due to an inherited impulse active at this precise stage of its life history. Other factors, external as well as internal, promote the readiness to migrate; but about these little is known, just as almost nothing is known about the mechanism that leads the salmon back to fresh water when it is ready to spawn. All that can be said at present is that at a certain point in its life history hereditary forces send the salmon back to the river of its birth.

Several salmon species travel a total of three or four thousand miles out to their feeding grounds and back again to their home streams to spawn. In at least the majority of cases, they return to the tributaries where they were hatched; and in this way distinct races have developed on different watersheds. Least of all is known about the ocean phase of salmon migration, because of the difficulty, in the fog and storms of the north Pacific a thousand miles off the coast of Alaska, of following a school of fish at ten or twenty fathoms. Probably the salmon, like a migratory bird, is able to rely on the sun, or rather the angles and direction of incidence of its rays, as an aid to navigation. Fishes have been shown to be capable of this feat, and even in darkness experimental salmon have maintained the same swimming direction as they had taken while they were oriented visually to the sun. In addition, there are distinct currents of temperature and salinity which the fish are able to detect.

No doubt many salmon never return, and many others still lose their way after reaching the shore regions, since they must find their own streams before they can spawn. Navigation from the sea to the river is thought to be accomplished by means of an acute sense of smell, which permits the fish to recognize the estuary of the river system to which its own stream belongs, causing it to turn upriver and then to take the correct turns all along the upstream journey. Experiments testing the reaction of salmon to oxygen and carbon dioxide concentrations, to temperature differences, and to the odor of particular streams, have shown that plugging the nostrils alone interfered with their orientation. The feat of finding a home stream by odor is remarkable evidence not only of the great acuity of fish senses but also of a good memory, since the fish must have recalled the stream odor, and perhaps other subsidiary clues, throughout its entire life.

Do rivers really have different odors? Man cannot distinguish between them by chemical clues, partly because he is not adapted to using his own sense of smell under water, as well as because it is far from keen to begin with; but any minnow can learn to distinguish by odor alone between two brooks, two kinds of aquatic plants, or two kinds of water beetles. Eels, for instance, have been shown to react to scented substances consisting of one part to eighteen million parts of water—a feat few bloodhounds could be expected to equal.

Eel Journeys

Exactly reversing the life cycle of the salmon, eels (*Anguilla*) undergo most of their development in fresh-water lakes and streams, returning to the sea to spawn. The mapping of their journeys, and especially the location of their spawning grounds, was a major achievement of marine biology. The journey to those spawning grounds begins in late summer or early fall, when eels on both sides of the Atlantic descend the rivers on their way to the sea. Up until then they are yellowish-green in color, with fairly small eyes; in fresh water they feed voraciously on fish and other aquatic life, so that they reach the sea with a fair supply of stored fat. They now cease to feed, and undergo physiological adjustments to the high salinity of their new environment, as well as an increase in the diameter of their eyes, apparently so as to be able to navigate in the subdued light of their deep-water travel route; and they also become silvery in color, like so many of the fishes of the high seas.

Swimming southward, probably following the countercurrents to the Gulf Stream, both European and American eels reach the Sargasso Sea, south of Bermuda, where at a depth of 200 fathoms the two species have adjacent but separate spawning areas. After spawning the parent eels die, and the eggs soon hatch into small, transparent larvae that are altogether unlike the adults. Although eels had been known from antiquity, it was not until 1896 that the anatomical relation between their young and adult forms was discovered. The credit for finally working out most of the eel's life history belongs to the Danish marine biologist Johannes Schmidt. Sailing counter to the Gulf Stream, and taking repeated hauls with fine-meshed nets as he traveled, he mapped the occurrence and relative sizes of eel larvae, to find that there was a decrease in size as the coast of Europe was left behind, and that the smallest of all were those in the Sargasso Sea. Evidently they drift northeast with the Gulf Stream, which has rightly been called the "Ocean River," for a period of close to three years. When they arrive offshore they are still flat and transparent, but they soon change into the small rounded "elvers" or glass eels that enter the estuaries, there to acquire their final adult form and migrate on upstream.

Continuations of the studies begun by Schmidt have shown that the spawning grounds of the American eel are slightly to the west of those of its European cousin, and it is presumed that the shorter distance traveled by the American eel accounts for its having a shorter larval life than the European eel. There is still some controversy over whether there are in fact two species or only one, with all European eels being merely the stray offspring of American parents, accidentally caught as larvae in the eastward drift of the Gulf Stream. But in that event it would also have to be assumed that the eels of Europe, though they follow their spawning urge and descend to the sea, invariably become lost before reaching the spawning grounds. This hypothesis does not appear likely in view of the differences, both anatomical and biochemical, between the two species.

The Sea Lamprey

Sea lampreys (*Petromyzon marinus*) have much the shape of an eel, though the resemblance is only superficial. Like the salmon, during their spawning migrations, they travel up rivers to reach the tributary streams that are their egg-laying sites. They are a primitive species, without the jaws, paired fins, and limb girdles typical of most fishes, and they have only a long median fin along the back; the tail fin, the brain, and the reproductive organs of the lamprey are also less complex than in other fishes. But at the same time they are specialized: the adult animal is an efficient parasite on other fishes, with a mouth consisting of a round suction funnel that can be closed and opened by a fore-and-aft movement of the tongue and that is equipped with horny, rasping teeth (Figure 45). In addition lampreys secrete an

Fig. 45 Lampreys attached to their victim, in this instance a creek chub. Photo from Michigan Institute for Fisheries Research.

anticoagulant which keeps the blood of their victims flowing while they feed.

The lamprey's earliest ancestors occur in fossils from the Ordovician period, about 450 million years ago; but it is not known at just what later date the lampreys acquired their specialized character, or when they invaded the temperate seas. Their spawning habit, at any rate, still keeps them tied to the gravelly streams and creeks that presumably were their original home and which, in the spring, they invade by the thousands to build their nests. In this manner they must have penetrated into Lake Ontario soon after it was formed. Through mutation the invaders evidently became adjusted to permanent residence in fresh water, taking the lake for their own private domain, although the falls at Niagara prevented them from ascending any farther.

The Great Lakes did not always drain into the St. Lawrence, but once had an outlet into the Mississippi, and before the lakes became established in their present shapes the vast amount of meltwater from the glaciers to the north had created numerous other drainage connections permitting fish to invade the lakes. From the southwest came the many forms typical of shallower and warmer waters, including minnows, suckers, the garpike, the bowfin, and the pickerel; from the east and west came the perch and such members of the sunfish family as the bass and the bluegill. The lamprey came from the east, but its numbers in Lake Ontario appear to have been kept in check, probably because only a few suitable spawning streams were available.

The building of canals around the rapids on the St. Lawrence, and of a series of locks over the Niagara escarpment, for the benefit of shipping, has also made it possible for new kinds of fish to reach the lakes beyond the falls. The sea lamprey was one of these. It was first taken in Lake Erie in 1921, less than a hundred years after the Welland Canal was built; by 1939 it had appeared in Lake Michigan, and by 1944 it had penetrated all the way to Lake Superior. Already having become adjusted to freshwater life by their residence in Lake Ontario, lampreys now populated all the lake basins—and, at spawning time, the rivers that flow into them as well.

In the spawning stream the female lamprey builds a nest,

carrying away stones—by means of suction with her buccal funnel—until she has hollowed out a small depression. Then she fastens herself onto a big stone just upstream from the nest, over which she lets her body drift while the male attaches himself to her. Thus partly entwined they wriggle back and forth over the nest, discharging sperm and eggs, the latter of which are small and adhesive, and which after being fertilized quickly sink to the bottom, to be covered with sand and silt. The adults, like those of several other fishes that make long spawning treks, die after spawning. The blind and toothless larvae leave the nests in search of quieter water, where they bury themselves in the bottom. There they remain stationary for several years. At this stage they are filter feeders, drawing the water with its microscopic organisms into the mouth by means of cilia, extracting the food, and letting the water out again through the gills. When they are about to change into the bloodsucking adult form they emerge from the bottom, let themselves be carried by the current into a lake, and search for a victim.

Upper Lake Huron, Lake Michigan, and especially Lake Superior offered ideal grounds for a lamprey population explosion. There are many sandy and gravelly spawning streams; the lake trout and the large whitefish were ideal victims; and there were no predators upon the lamprey itself. Soon the new arrival had become a formidable competitor with man—whose efforts to cope with this and with similar problems he has unwittingly brought upon himself will be the subject of a later chapter.

PART III.

Moving Waters and Man

7

Rivers and History

For hundreds of millions of years animals had been coming to the streams and rivers of the world to drink, to bathe, to find their food, to set up breeding territories, or to build nests or dens. Here and there they had slightly modified the streamside by making a path down to the water, or the channel itself by the widening of a hippopotamus wallow or the building of a beaver dam. Then, somewhere between a million and five hundred thousand years ago, bands of a new kind of predator began to appear at the watering places of the grazers and browsers. These protohuman creatures walked on two legs; more vociferous than lions or leopards, they carried on their communal hunting with shouts and grunts that eventually became words; and they extended the power of their forelimbs by the use of clubs and spears.

A troop of these hunters might have had a territory

comprising an entire river valley with its bluffs, lakes, and tributary streams. Like the animals they hunted, they would migrate frequently, following the river's course, but being less well adapted than many other animals to going without drinking for more than a few hours, they did not stray far from the water, and at first made no impact on the river itself or on the plants growing along its shores.

But several hundred thousand years later their descendants had developed a more sedentary way of life as a result of what was perhaps man's greatest cultural advance, the domestication of plants and of animals. Their communal life also had developed beyond mere cooperation in the hunt; the campsites by a clear spring, or on a solid hummock of land near the shellfish beds in an estuarine marsh, had become settled villages. The earliest agricultural settlements appear to have been those along tributaries of the upper Euphrates and Tigris rivers, and are now dated at around 7000 B.C.

The four valleys that were the center of the earliest civilizations—those of the Nile, the Indus, the twin rivers Euphrates and Tigris, and the Hwang Ho—are subject to heavy floods at regular times of the year, with rises of from fifteen to twenty feet at the crest of the flood. At some prehistoric period man took to building canals and dams, thus increasing the area of his croplands. In ancient Mesopotamia the earliest canal system put seven million acres under cultivation; the entire acreage of irrigated land in the American Southwest today is only about four times as large. The great river cultures became the granaries of the ancient world, supplying food not only to the inhabitants of the valleys but also to many others beyond them.

The kind of agriculture made possible by irrigation and the domestication of grain-bearing grasses—wheat, barley, and rice—was permanent and demanded a large-scale cooperation that led in turn to a closely knit social organization. Children, no longer the burden they had been to a band of hunters, became desirable as helpers. Thus the new settled life along the river, and perhaps a temporary food surplus, may have led to the first modest but permanent increase in population.

The cultivation of irrigated lands that tied man to the river valleys led invariably to the development of cities with their granaries, market places, administrative centers, and religious rites. In the city separate administrative and ruling classes arose, who were exempt from manual labor, and under whose direction the refinements of art and culture came into being. By degrees the rulers of cities extended their dominion over entire river valleys and watersheds, thus establishing the foundations of ancient empires whose influence was eventually to spread over still greater areas.

Irrigation and Water Power

To maintain a permanent system of irrigation along a river with seasonal high and low stages, the water had to be raised, at times over a dyke, at times to still higher ground. Among the several machines invented for this purpose were the primitive water wheels. A certain flow is necessary to turn a large paddlewheel with sufficient force to send the raised water trickling into a trough and thence into the fields. Where the flow is not sufficient, the wheel has to be powered by man or one of the animals he has domesticated.

Still more primitive devices for raising water probably consisted first of a bag of skin attached to a rope of plant fibers, and later of pottery vessels such as are described in early Babylonic writings. In ancient Babylonia the faster flow of the rivers as compared to those of Egypt, and the contours of the land, made possible an irrigation depending largely on the flow of gravity, whereas in the delta of the Nile large amounts of water had to be lifted from the slower-flowing arms of the river. To accomplish this the early Egyptians placed on the bank a pivot that supported a crossbeam with a water bucket at one end and a counterweight at the other that allowed the raising of the load with a minimum of effort. This lever arrangement, called a shadoof, is pictured on clay seals dating back to 2500 B.C., and is still in use today.

Another means of raising water is the treadmill, operated by stepping on a series of rotating pedals along the rim of a small wheel, to which is connected a larger one carrying a series of buckets or scoops. An adaptation of this same device, built on the bicycle principle, is still in use along the Mekong, where it existed long before bicycles had been introduced from Europe (Figure 46). Along the waterways of Cambodia and Vietnam a young peasant couple may often be seen treading away at the waterwheel in the shade of an isolated tree. The wheel drives a chain of upright plates resembling a caterpillar tread, which raises the water and sends it through a wooden gutter into a field ten feet above the level of the river. Although each plate moves only a small amount of water, the total effect is a steady flow.

Day after day the same couple will be at their job of irrigation for an hour or so in the morning and again in the cool of the evening. They chat with one another as they sit on their perches above the wheel, in evident enjoyment of the chore; after all, it removes them for a while from the presence of in-laws and children—a respite of privacy that must be welcome in this land of crowded households, the traditional warmth of Asian family affection notwithstanding.

Related to the simple machines that raise the water to irrigate the land are the water mills used for grinding grain or working metal, which are often cited as prime movers by historians of technology. The invention of every new prime mover—the steam engine is one example—has meant

FIG. 46 Irrigating Chinese rice fields with a treadmill—a practice that continues to this day. From a seventeenth-century painting at the Freer Gallery, Washington, D.C.

more available energy and another technological stride forward by mankind. But for the major part of his existence thus far *Homo sapiens* has been his own prime mover, dependent entirely upon the energy stored in his own muscles. The domestication of animals supplied a new source of tractive power, but it was not until less than three thousand years ago that man began to harness rapid streams for that most recurrent chore of every primitive household, the grinding of grain. The earliest mills were small, and their output of energy and hence of flour was low. They consisted of flat, circular millstones, connected by a vertical shaft with a horizontal paddlewheel that was turned by the current of the stream. This invention, simple as it was, must have given the early housewife not only relief from drudgery but a comparatively great amount of leisure. Having to grind or pound kernels by hand meant—as it still does in many parts of the world even now—that little if any flour could be stored, and that the work had to be done every day.

At about the time of Christ an unknown inventor revolutionized milling by adding to a paddlewheel on a horizontal shaft a set of gears that coupled it with the vertical shaft bearing the millstones. Thus the mill as it is known today—called the Vitruvian mill after the Roman historian who first described it—came into being. After millponds, dams, chutes, reservoirs, and aqueducts had been perfected in order to take full advantage of this development, the overshot wheel—as it is also called—was capable of generating as much as forty or even sixty horsepower. During the Middle Ages such mills sprang up in central and northern Europe and in China, where their development was favored by the relatively uniform rainfall more than it had been in the regions of intermittent rainfall which had been the first centers of civilization.

Gradually the size of reservoirs and dams increased, until finally, less than a hundred years ago, the hydraulic turbine for converting mechanical energy into electricity had been evolved, drawing for its mechanics on features both of the Vitruvian mill and of the more ancient horizontal paddlewheel. Since Edison's invention of the incandescent lamp, electricity has come to be taken so completely for granted in our own country that we are unable to function without it. In the hilly and mountainous regions of America, Europe, and the Soviet Union nearly all electric power is obtained from the driving force of water held behind dams. In most other parts of the world the power of rivers is still scarcely used, even though the potential amount is estimated to be many hundred times what is now being tapped. But although many millions still go to sleep when the sun has set, regardless of the hour, plans are being made to dam many tropical rivers, so that it may not be long before men in the remotest corners of the earth will be turning night into day simply by the flick of a switch.

The River Travels of Man

Man travels farther and faster than any animal. Some of his mammalian relatives migrate long distances to follow a seasonal abundance of food; others avoid the rigors of winter by storing fat, lowering their temperature, and going into hibernation; but man is far less strictly governed by his external environment. Early man migrated on foot, as diverse remains from the stone age show, but when he began to domesticate animals his mobility on land was increased many times over; and as soon as his tool-making capacity had led to the invention of boats, the rivers began beckoning him to explore what lay around the next bend.

The first boats on the Nile were probably bundles of rushes tied together, on which a man rode between two sheaves that were the archetype of gunwales. On the twin rivers of Mesopotamia, where papyrus and other rushes were lacking, men buoyed themselves with inflated animal skins and kicked their way across the river. Later the skin floats were tied together to support rafts. Similar early devices for river navigation appeared in the arid Balkans and the American Southwest. A further step in the use of hides was to stretch them over a wooden scaffold like those of the Eskimo kayak and umiak (the larger boat in which women rode), which were in turn the forerunners of the modern canvas canoe. Where there were forests men hollowed out trees to produce dugout canoes—an idea possibly suggested by large pieces of bark such as may have supported hunters or warriors on the water. The various types of primitive boats that have sprung up independently all over the globe clearly indicate the close alliance of the earliest inventions to the nature of available materials.

The wooden boat was the easiest to enlarge and make seaworthy; therefore it grew in size and assumed many shapes. The invention of oars and sails notwithstanding, it was only the comparatively recent development of the steam engine and the steel hull that further enlarged the scope of boat-building, leading to the gigantic ocean liners of today. Traveling upstream was difficult and often slower than following the same route on horseback or even on foot. Furthermore, river travel was often just as seasonal as any animal migration because of winter ice and spring floods. Before the days of the railroad and the horseless carriage, men along the vast water network of the Mississippi anxiously awaited the coming of spring and the big ice push from the north. Moorings were reinforced, and the flat-bottomed floating palaces that hibernated in St. Louis were secured in their docks with thick iron chains. The ice push began usually in early March, when the floes would advance, slowly turning like huge millstones, and pushing over one another with a noise like the firing of distant cannon. In places they would be compressed between the arches of a bridge; some would be crushed, while others would circle more rapidly, to float out into the open stream again and vanish on their way toward the south. As the floes became smaller and smaller, changing in color from white to greenish grey, they would break, worn down by their long journey, to disappear completely by the time the first magnolia trees appeared along the shore. Up until late in the last century newspapers still carried announcements to prospective patrons that such a steamer as the *Great Republic* or the *Robert E. Lee* would begin its journey on such and such a day to Cairo, Vicksburg, and New Orleans, or upstream to Pittsburgh or Cincinnati.

The Ohio, inasmuch as it drains an area greater than is drained by the Mississippi above the mouth of the Missouri, and lies in a zone of greater rainfall, carries nearly a quarter of all the waters that flow into the Gulf of Mexico. Its more or less westward course and its eminent navigability predestined *La Belle Rivière*, as it was originally called by the French, to become a historic highway for the white man's westward migration on the new continent. Nearly a hundred and fifty years were to pass after La Salle had first glimpsed the great river around 1670, before the valley it drained was settled by adventurous men from the east. The first travelers on the Ohio descended it in canoes and pirogues; then came barges, likewise traveling only downstream; but after Pittsburgh and other cities had been founded in the upper Ohio Valley, a craft was needed that could make the upstream journey. For this purpose the famous keelboats had running boards extending from end to end along their sides; on these the crew would walk slowly, carrying poles with which to push the boat upstream. At times, especially at high water, the shoreward crew would catch hold of the bushes or branches of trees on the river bank in order to pull the keelboat upstream—whence the word "bushwhack." Such keelboats did not exceed fifty feet in length and could thus ascend small rivers even up to some portages; in their own way they were as important in spreading people and goods as the steamers that followed them. In addition there were also the great barges that carried forty or fifty tons of freight and were manned by as many men, who helped to pull them upstream from the shores or who manned rows of oars to augment the force provided by the sails. Craft similar to all these were once found on all larger rivers; on some they make up the bulk of traffic even today.

A stretch of river more famous than any other for its incomparable scenery, its treacherously varied waters, and its dangers to navigation is the series of gorges along the Yangtze Kiang below Chunking in China. In the nearly vertical rock walls that contain the curves of the great river, towpaths have been hewn as high as five hundred feet above the level of low water. One junk can overtake a slower craft by raising its towline over that of the other; and although to facilitate this maneuver the ropes are attached to the mast instead of the bow, they may still become entangled. At such times the attempt to loosen them makes them vibrate from rock to rock, often sweeping past a group of coolies towing another boat and threatening to hurl them into the abyss below. The towpaths are lined with tablets and cairns, in lieu of tombs, commemorating just such misfortunes. The barges thus towed have no keel, but merely a pair of sideboards to enable them to sail upstream in the slower portions of the river, making good use of the summer monsoon as it sweeps upstream through the valley. Oars are used, and also stakes, as on the Ohio keelboats; and pilots directing the upstream journey are skilled at taking advantage of the countercurrents near the shore. Often, though, only towing will move the craft; then the entire crew is set ashore to man the long towrope braided from slit bamboo. Each coolie puts his shoulder into a kind of harness, so fashioned that he can slip out of it with ease. Even steamboats in the Yangtze gorges need a towing crew that may consist of hundreds of men, manning eight or more ropes.

Most rivers already had two-way traffic by the time recorded history began. At an even earlier time rivers gave direction to the spread of peoples; some, among them the

Yangtze and the Hwang Ho of China, led the conquerors of new lands from the hearts of continents to the sea. Others directed migrations inland; one such, the Mackenzie, lying in a portion of the Canadian Arctic that was unglaciated through most of the last quarter of a million years, funneled toward the south the ancestors of certain tribes of American Indians after they had crossed the land bridge over the Bering Straits.

Now that man has explored and mapped nearly the entire globe, rivers have lost their importance as landmarks in the opening up of new regions. They are also less important as arteries of travel, although they still carry large amounts of freight. In places ground travel routes also still follow rivers—particularly in mountainous country, where the course of a stream is often the best one for a railroad or superhighway to follow. Nevertheless, even though such problems as that of upstream navigation have been solved, the relation between man and the moving water has become not less but more complex. Some of the problems yet unsolved are new and man-made; others are natural events as old as the rivers themselves. Of the latter, none is more awesome than the yearly rise and fall to which all rivers are subject, and which throughout human history has conferred benefit as well as disaster.

Floods

Without floods the development of human civilization in Egypt, in Mesopotamia, and in China could not have taken place. Though dams have long been built to control them, man also coped with floods by learning to live with them—as he still does in many parts of the tropics where the climate is warm and shelter can be quickly built. Of course, floods also occur in the temperate zone—the Ohio, the Tennessee, and the Missouri are only a few of America's flood-prone rivers—but in temperate areas, in part because housing there needs to be more permanent than in the tropics, and in part because industries and other valuable property are threatened by floods, Western man has developed intensive flood control measures. He has also coerced his rivers into regulated channels and has done as much as was in his power to prevent floods, rather than to roll with their punches as people in the tropics still do. An instance of the latter are the people of the valley of the Mekong, for whom rice and fish, the staples of diet in Southeast Asia, are both the legacy of the floods, and who continue to gear their lives to the yearly rise and fall of the river (Figure 47). At high water a layer of rich mud settles on the flooded land, and the use of fertilizer becomes superfluous. When the waters recede, the ground is ready either for

FIG. 47 Collapsible houses on a lake near the Mekong—the great river of Cambodia. Photo by the author.

seeding or for setting out young rice plants. In addition some water is retained by means of dykes and sluices.

When the water level falls it leaves behind, conveniently beached on dry land, the boat that needs repair, with ample time to repair it. In the following year, the river will rise again to set it afloat. At the same time it will inundate forests consisting of trees adapted to having their trunks submerged for part of the year. Here, during the dry season, the villager may gather firewood which he may float out on rafts when the river rises. At flood time wild animals congregate on higher ground and hunting becomes easier.

The final gift of the high water is to deliver a wealth of fish through the inundated forests and shrublands, where they grow big and fat. As a result the region of the lower Mekong was for decades the chief source of proteins for the dense populations of Vietnam and Java. Catching the fish is no problem; a fisherman only needs to build barrages to intercept them as they leave with the receding waters.

The fishermen's villages, which are built either on barges or on stilts, are the prototype of modern prefabricated housing. The walls and floors are sections of bamboo thatchwork, tied to upright supports which are sunk into the soft ground. At low water there is fishing only in the center of a lake that may be less than three feet deep, whereas in the fall, after the rains, the same lake will be twenty-five or more feet deep and twice its former area. The simplest way of dealing with these extremes is to move the whole village; in the new site it does not take long to have the houses ready again.

At all seasons the Mekong is alive with junks that carry vivid patchwork sails, and with little, gaily painted, flat-bottomed river steamers—their upper and lower decks full of sarong-clad travelers—as well as with fishermen's sampans operated by brown men in black tunics, each standing in the bow, patiently lifting and lowering and lifting again a large fork strung with thin black netting. In between the forks the jumping fish sparkle like jewels in the strong morning sun. Here and there the activity is interrupted by a long stretch of glassily calm, oily brown water, where there are neither boats nor people, and where the brown expanse is divided from the bone-dry blue sky above by a thin green strip of garden landscape, fringed at the horizon with the clustering tops of sugar palms.

The waters of the Mekong generally belong to the government, and exploitation rights are leased once a year to the highest bidder. A reserve of ready cash, the right connections, and some greasing of palms will permit an entrepreneur to lease many square miles of water for the placement of fish traps. Most big fishing operators sublease a part or all of their rights to smaller operators and make a handsome profit in so doing.

The fish are concentrated in the main channel when the water is low, awaiting the beginning of the rainy season and their spawning period. With the rising waters the young are carried over the vast inundated lands, where shallow temporary lakes and temporarily drowned forests become veritable hothouse cultures of protozoan, plankton, worm, and insect life. In the midst of this abundance the fish grow fast. When the waters recede and the fish are returning to the river, there is no creek or flowage of any kind that does not have a bamboo barrage with a catching cage at its downstream end. Out of the more than a thousand species of fish that live there, between eighty and a hundred kinds are marketed. Most of these are members of the minnow and catfish families, and some are so large that their tails drag in the mud between the pairs of men who carry them on poles strung through their gills.

Some of the Mekong's fishes have become adapted to staying behind in the lowlands even when the waters recede. Parts of the gills or mouth cavities have developed into lunglike structures, permitting the fish to breathe air. The same species have developed sturdy fins, enabling them to walk overland for miles from a drying water hole to a wetter one. (The first sight of a three-foot fish walking across the road on a moonlit night may cause the observer to review his living habits.) As the water of the river recedes farther, these fish bury themselves, finding the moist places that flood first and dry last, in which to estivate during the dry season.

The larger fishing sites are marked by clusters of houseboats and huts. At the river's edge there are drying platforms for salted fish, enveloped in the powerful smell emanating from the piles of fish offal. The site is dominated by traps and barricades whose buttresses and wings suggest those of a river fortress (Figure 48). High above the river a catwalk connects several platforms furnished with altars, flags, and banners, designed to reassure the spirits above and below the waters. The platforms are forbidden territory to women, since it is believed that a woman's presence there would ruin the fishing or have even worse consequences for the encampment–a superstition that gives the fishermen a chance to get away by themselves for a while.

When the downstream fish migration is at its peak the cages into which the fish are funneled may be lifted at regular intervals all around the clock. Those fish that are not kept alive to be sold fresh are treated on the spot by women who sit in long open sheds built over the water. Here they cut up the fish, letting the heads and entrails fall through the slats of the floor into the river below; the bodies are then split, placed in brine, and dried in the sun–a way of preserving fish that dates back to ancient Egypt.

Another method is to place the fish in vats with large amounts of salt, weight them down with stones, and leave them to ferment. After a few months the vats are tapped to yield a clear golden liquid of extraordinarily high nitro-

Fig 48 Fish-catching barrage across a tributary of the Mekong River in Cambodia. Photo from U.S. Agency for International Development.

gen content. So nourishing is this *Tuk Trey* (a Cambodian name meaning "fish water"), that a French physician used it successfully as a substitute for milk in raising abandoned babies. The ancient Romans produced a similar liquid, equally salty, pungent, and tasty, which like *Tuk Trey* was used in soups or as a sauce for meat.

Undoubtedly the most pungent way of preserving the river's bounty—also of ancient origin and widespread throughout the Orient—is to turn fish into cheese. The recipe calls for certain thumb-long, short-lived fishes which occur by the billions. After these have been cleaned, cut, and mixed with salt, the mixture is left to rot in a vat. After six months—or for the best results even longer—the action of various bacteria will have turned it into a whitish paste, compounded of proteins and amino acids, and laced with calcium from the softened bones. The odor is very strong, but approached without prejudice and bearing in mind that Western cheese is of comparable origin, it can be delicious.

The people of Laos and Cambodia, and above all of Vietnam, are now becoming so numerous that they cannot continue in their age-old ways. Their leap from the past into the present involves stricter control of the river and the land around it. In the process they have burned large tracts of inundated forests that were once fish nurseries, and the ensuing erosion has led in turn to the rapid silting in of lakes and rivers, followed inevitably by a decline in the fishes of the region. The rise and fall of this and other tropical rivers will be further regulated, the land will be irrigated instead of being flooded naturally, and fifty years from now the Mekong may have dams and a navigable channel into Laos, with locks bypassing several rapids. The river will generate hydropower, and modern methods of agriculture will boost the rice harvest to several times its present volume. Although the people will still eat fish, most of these will be grown from selected stock in artificial ponds.

The Problem of Pollution

It is sometimes argued that the influence of man on his surroundings is merely one more biological force, differing only in degree from the instinctive habits of beavers or the tendency of sphagnum moss to fill a bog—or, conversely, that man is exerting a set of novel forces, no more comparable in kind than in degree with the processes of biological evolution. In any event, there can be no question of the rate at which man-made changes have occurred. Their dimensions are matters of historical record, with the changing rivers as prime witnesses.

The Ohio River is a classic case. Before 1800, travelers who made their way west told of wooded, vine-hung islands, and of forested hills coming down to the water's edge. In places there were high, steep banks dense with overhanging trees; in others the valley broadened into rich bottomland. The forest edge was studded with flowering bushes, fragrant with blossom in the spring, luscious with berries in the fall. Flocks of wild geese swarmed upon the water; turkeys and quail abounded on the shore, as did deer and other forest animals. A hunting party could easily bring in several hundred squirrels from one expedition, and kills of more than a thousand were reported. There were bears too, but they were wary even before the white man came. Flattened patches in the grass where they had rested and sunned themselves, and rotten logs torn to pieces in quest of ants, often indicated their presence. The forest trees were straight and high, and were of many different kinds.

A century and a half later, a description of the same area would have read as follows: The banks were littered with tin cans, with pieces of plaster in bizarre shapes, and with remnants of torn-down or left-over construction; here and there abandoned cars turned upside down lay rusting. Old gunny sacks hung limply on branches of brush remaining from the last high water, and bottles of all shapes were scattered up and down the shore. Even in July the elm trees along the shore road had lost most of their leaves, and the few that remained were yellow. The sun shone blurred through the smog that lay heavily over the valley. Where in days past a hunting party might have gone ashore to shoot squirrels, teen-agers from factory towns sat on the debris, aiming with slingshots at the many rats that scurried in and out of their hideaways among the garbage. Every now and then one was hit and fell into the river, adding its carcass to the already polluted waters of the Ohio.

The pollution of streams is not new. As soon as there were settlements in the river valleys, their wastes began to be emptied into the streams. The towns of the ancient Indus Valley civilization appear to have been provided with a kind of sewer system; yet from time to time these Indian towns appear to have been abandoned to escape the effects of pollution. The drains, it is now assumed, were storm sewers and did nothing to alleviate the accumulation of organic wastes in the rivers. Conditions did not improve through the ages. Imperial Rome and Elizabethan London were equally unsanitary places. And when the workshops of Europe before the industrial revolution were supplanted by the factories of the nineteenth century, the rivers continued to be used for the dumping of wastes as well as for an industrial water supply. It is no wonder that before the advent of the first sewage treatment plants late in the nineteenth century, the rivers near all large towns should have been foul-smelling and unsightly. The following verse, found on a boardroom table after a meeting of the Mersey and Irwell Joint River Committees in 1901, describes the situation in England at the turn of the century:

> If with a stick you stir well
> The poor old river Irwell
> Very sick of the amusement
> You will very soon become
> For fetid bubbles rise and burst
> But that is really not the worst
> For little birds can hop about
> Dry-footed in the scum.

And at about the same time, a branch of the Des Plaines River near Chicago was reported to have become covered with a scum so thick that it could support the weight of a man.

Although the course of history leads in a straight line from the stone-age tanner who scraped his furs into a stream to the river-polluting tannery, oil refinery, or plating plant of the twentieth century, there is one important difference between the two. As recently as a century and a half ago, next to nothing was known of the consequences of pouring factory wastes into rivers. The factory owner of today no longer has this excuse. The nature of pollution is now understood, even though the problem itself is far from being solved.

8

Repairing the Damage

The Natural History of Pollution

A healthy river does not need always to be clean; some streams are naturally turbid at certain seasons. On the other hand, a stream may be clear and blue—to all appearances an aquatic paradise—and yet contain certain chemicals which have made it a biological desert, from which all living things have disappeared. Many industrial wastes contain irritants or poisons which aquatic animals take up just as they do dissolved oxygen. In the gills of fishes and other stream-dwelling animals, sometimes only one thin cell layer separates the blood or other body fluids from the surrounding water. Some chemicals diffuse through the gills, to act on the internal organs; others clog or injure the gill surfaces, impairing respiration and leading finally to death by suffocation.

Fishes are in some ways better off than rooted plants or less mobile invertebrates, since they are equipped by their acute senses of smell and taste to detect certain noxious substances, and can then swim away from them. Still other substances, though, are intoxicating to fish; among these are cresol wastes, which interfere with their balance and coordination of movement. Copper sulfate, a typical metal-plating waste, acts as an anesthetic, so rapidly that by the time a fish has detected its presence it can no longer swim out of the danger zone.

At the opposite extreme from chemically poisoned rivers are those in which an excess of organic material has led to pollution. Indeed, the line between a polluted body of water and a very fertile one is not easily drawn. A river that a waterworks engineer might describe as very rich will be indignantly described as polluted by the smallmouth-bass fisherman whose favorite quarry has disappeared. The cause of such a disappearance is fundamentally the same as that leading to the winterkill of fishes in a eutrophic lake—namely that there is not enough dissolved oxygen.

Why should the enrichment of the water lead to a depletion of oxygen? Behind this seeming paradox is the nature of the process of decomposition. Human wastes and household refuse discharged as sewage are made up largely of complex chemical compounds, which in water are broken down by the ever-present bacteria into simple chemicals—nitrates, phosphates, and carbonates. In this process the bacteria use up large quantities of dissolved oxygen from the water. When sewage becomes excessive, the indigenous stream life loses out in the competition with the bacteria for the supply of oxygen. The river is then taken over by organisms that can live on unoxygenated decomposition products, such as hydrogen sulfide, and which in turn produce still other evil-smelling and noxious gases, such as methane. Black, gelatinous colonies of algae form an unsightly floating mat over the sludge; the air becomes polluted, and discolors the leaves of trees and the paint on neighboring houses.

Any river, of course, will tend to purify itself as it moves downstream from the source of pollution. Chemical wastes will be gradually diluted, the rate of purification depending on the amount of clear water available to the stream. The same is true of bacteria in water polluted by sewage. Luckily, under natural conditions the coliform bacteria and other parasites responsible for diseases of the human digestive tract die within a certain length of time after being exposed in the water of a stream.

Usually a river will go through several distinct stages as it flows away from a source of organic pollution. Above the source, the stream may be healthy and clear, with a community of insect larvae, snails, crayfish, minnows and other small fishes, and perhaps a few bass. A proportion of from seven to nine parts per million of dissolved oxygen in the water will be more than adequate for any animal that happens to live there.

At the junction with the sewer, where the zone of pollution begins, the water turns bluish and turbid, there are bits of floating sludge, and the air smells of hydrogen sulfide and methane. Next comes a zone where the animal species are limited to those adapted to cope with a severe reduction or total absence of oxygen. Among these are the rattailed maggot, *Eristalis tenax*, and the wriggler of the sewage mosquito, *Culex pipiens*, both of which are equipped with a snorkel-like air tube that pierces the surface film and takes in atmospheric oxygen. Red sludgeworms of the genus *Tubifex* will also be abundant. These worms, of which there may be several thousand per square inch, make a heavy demand on whatever residual oxygen the river still has to offer. In addition, they pass settled organic matter through their guts at a staggering rate: an individual worm, although it is only an inch and a half long, and no thicker than a needle, may accumulate up to six inches of fecal threads in a day.

Water becomes recharged with oxygen while it flows, and attached or suspended aquatic plants contribute to the oxygen supply through photosynthesis. But photosynthesis goes on only in daylight; at night the plants themselves have to take up oxygen to live. It may therefore happen during the night that fish tolerant of low oxygen conditions, such as carp, which come upstream to feed on sludgeworms in a zone where the recovery of oxygen takes place during the day, die by thousands of suffocation because there is no longer any oxygen at all.

At some distance below a sewage outflow the nutrient-rich environment of partly oxidized compounds produces a third zone, well suited to the growth of such attached algae as *Cladophora*, which form long fronds and color the river bright green. If the flow slows down at that point, the great supply of nitrogen and phosphorus may lead to a condition in which the water resembles a green broth, with the color and consistency of pea soup (Figure 49). For reasons that are not well understood, these dense growths—known as pulses or algal blooms—sometimes produce substances poisonous to livestock and wild mammals, and even to fish. Fortunately such occurrences are rare.

At last, many miles below the town, in the normal course of events the river returns to a state that may be described as clean. The amount of runoff, the temperature, the sources of re-aeration available, and the speed of the current all govern the rate at which self-purification can take place. Where the river is meandering, where there are natural or artificial pools, and where water is diverted from the streambed for agriculture or industry, the capacity of a stream to purify itself is limited accordingly.

But all too often a river is not allowed a sufficient breath-

FIG. 49 A river below a source of organic pollution breaks out into a dense bloom of algae. Photo by Alfred F. Bartsch, U.S. Public Health Service.

ing spell between one source of pollution and another for the process of self-purification to be completed naturally. This is where sewage treatment comes in. Various methods are employed: among them are settling tanks, activated sludge processes, and a system of trickling filters over sinter beds covered with green algae that act as suppliers of oxygen. In each process the aim is to give bacteria a chance to digest and oxidize as much of the sewage as possible before it reaches the river. However, even the most efficient treatment still leaves 10 per cent or more of the load of organic material unoxidized, so that a certain demand of the river's own supply of oxygen is inevitable. Where a steam power plant discharges waste water near a sewer entry, the temperature of the river will be raised and all biological processes, including the action of bacteria, will be accelerated accordingly. Often, especially at the seasonal stage of low water, a river may be so depleted by use in industry or irrigation that nearly its entire flow below a town may be made up of sewage effluents.

Sanitary engineers regard forty volumes of water to one of sewage as a fairly adequate dilution. And since it is estimated that an average per capita of a hundred gallons of liquid containing organic wastes are now being discharged into streams every day, the problem is clearly staggering. With the rapid increase in population since World War II, many sewage plants have become inadequate. Their annual maintenance alone now runs from one to three dollars and a half per capita; and to build a new plant now costs in the neighborhood of twenty-five dollars a person.

Nevertheless, the problem of disposing of human wastes is not new, nor is it confined to our own country. In Japan and China, where people live crowded together with a density unknown in America, and where they must eke out a sustenance from far poorer soil, human wastes have long been used as fertilizer. Around Berlin, sewage-irrigated market gardens once produced prime vegetables, and the city of Munich was famous for the fat and tasty carp grown in its sewage ponds.

Even in America, some cities have dealt constructively with the pollution problem by turning their sewage into fertilizer. The plant food Melorganite, marketed by the Milwaukee municipal system, is an example. Such enterprises remain isolated, and have not been financially successful largely because of culture-bound objections to such extreme forms of conservation. However, further experiments of the same kind are under way; at the University of California at Berkeley, for example, sewage is being converted into a dried and purified algal extract for use as a feed additive for cattle.

An ingenious system for sewage treatment developed in Communist China, which was recently displayed at a trade fair in southern Asia, collected decomposition gases for use in cooking and illumination, and converted liquid and solid wastes into a powder to be used on the fields. The health hazards of such a system are minimal, and its virtue is the wise husbandry of organic fertilizer compounds through repeated re-use. Even in the West, self-contained sewage systems for family residences, operated with a minimum of water to produce dehydrated sludge, will no doubt one day be perfected, along with improved systems for disposing of municipal wastes.

The Ohio Compact

In the meantime, to prevent large rivers from deteriorating, cooperation between states or even between nations is frequently necessary. Such joint action is difficult to carry out; but even so, some once sadly polluted rivers are now on the way to recovery thanks to the voluntary cooperation of the people along their shores. A notable example is the Ohio, whose appearance in the 1940's has been described. When it had become difficult to produce safe drinking water from the river, and when air pollution from factories and smelters along its shores had become so severe that paint peeled off the houses in their vicinity, the states concerned finally approached the problem by forming an interstate compact. In 1948, after delays due to problems of state legislation and to wartime difficulties, the states of Illinois, Indiana, Kentucky, New York, Ohio, Pennsylvania, Tennessee, and West Virginia joined in setting up the Ohio River Valley Water Sanitation District and the Ohio River Valley Water Sanitation Commission (ORSANCO) for the abatement and control of pollution.

Some idea of the magnitude of the task that faced the Commission may be conveyed by statistics. Over 20 million people live in the region surrounding the 1,000-mile stretch of the Ohio covered by the compact; industry uses and returns over 10 billion gallons of water a day, and 250 million gallons daily are taken from the river; as much as a quarter of the entire river's flow is sometimes in use for cooling by the power plants of the region. The Commission has reported that in 1950, out of twenty fairly evenly spaced stations along the Ohio only three showed a bacterial limit within a range desirable for water supply purposes. At the other stations, the water was difficult if not impossible to treat without making it impalatable. And no wonder, since when the compact was formed less than one per cent of the three and a half million people living directly along the river had the benefit of sewage treatment. Today 95 per cent of the Ohio's riparian population are or shortly will be served by treatment plants now operating or under construction. The remaining sewage problems along the Ohio mainly concern towns with populations of less than 5,000.

In places, industrial pollution of the Ohio and its tributaries is still a shocking offense against the common interest (Figure 50). To spot such transgressions the Commission has installed a robot monitoring system whose complicated machinery will eventually operate in forty places along the river, analyzing the water on a round-the-clock basis. The results of these automatic tests are to be telemetered to a central office in Cincinnati, where a continuous record of data on oxygen, as well as on temperature and solar radiation, will be maintained.

So far the compact has worked well; legal experts regard it as a good instrument, and it has the approval of most of the people in the valley. The Commission deals not only with mainstream problems but also with those that arise on interstate tributaries. As a result the several states have been more conscious of their internal water situation, and are less prone to lag behind in cleaning and repair jobs on their own rivers and streams. Even so, the Ohio River will never again be what it was before its valley was settled. Parts of

Fig. 50 Industrial wastes flowing into the Kanawha, a tributary of the Ohio. Photo from ORSANCO.

the main stream and some tributaries in the compact area are still smelly, the silt load remains high, oil slicks still occur, and tests for coliform bacteria still show regional health hazards. Education and communal action provided the key to the Ohio's partial recovery. If these had been applied earlier, starting with the tributaries rather than the main stream, faster and perhaps better results might have been achieved.

Land Use and Flood Control

No less complex, and equally demanding of cooperation on a large scale, are the problems of flood control. Clearly the immediate cause of any flood is a sudden increase in the volume of a stream caused by rain or the melting of ice and snow; but the terrain, the composition of the soil, and the nature of the plant cover are of great importance, and may determine whether or not a disastrous flood follows a heavy rain.

Under normally favorable conditions, a gentle rain will soak into the soil rather than flow over its surface. Afterward, while the soil remains moist, water will evaporate into the air from it, as well as from the surfaces of ponds and from fields and woodlands. In fact, plants give off relatively more moisture than does the soil, or even than water surfaces do. Water from the soil is ceaselessly being absorbed by the roots of a plant, to rise in a steady stream through the stem or trunk to the leaves, where it evaporates through minute pores called stomata. An acre of red maples in a moist habitat, for example, may give off water equivalent to a rainfall of twenty-eight inches a year; and corn plants during their growing season transpire enough moisture to cover the field where they stand to a depth of fifteen inches.

After rain has begun to fall, plants will intercept it for a while, preventing it from reaching the ground until the foliage is thoroughly moistened—as anyone knows who has ever taken shelter from a sudden rain under a grove of trees. What falls directly upon the ground will at first seep in to fill the minute soil spaces. Only when the ground is thoroughly soaked—or, as hydrologists put it, when field moisture capacity has been reached—does surplus water begin to run off, eventually to flow overland into the nearest stream. This runoff will occur first, of course, on bare ground such as is found along roadsides. When there are no leaves on the trees and the ground is frozen—thus preventing any infiltration of the soil—torrential early spring rains may lead to a rapid rise in the water level and to catastrophic flooding.

When the soil has reached field moisture capacity down to the level of the underground water table, some additional moisture may still percolate through it, especially if the soil material is porous. As a result the water table will then rise temporarily, producing a subterranean flow into the streams of the region. This underground seepage feeds streams more gently and evenly than does the water reaching them from the surface of the ground. The importance of the composition of the soil in checking floods thus becomes evident.

The size, arrangement, and density of the soil particles all go into determining how much water can infiltrate into a given plot of ground. Clay is extremely dense, and absorbs very little. Virgin land usually has the most favorable porosity. Long and intensive cultivation can lead to a depletion of organic matter and to denser packing; as a result the water-holding capacity of the soil is decreased, runoff increases, and erosion follows.

Proper land use and flood control are intimately related. In many instances, especially on wooded slopes, the best use that can be made of land is to leave it under its natural cover to serve for recreation. Likewise, the water-retaining properties of cultivated land can be increased by strip-cropping, contour plowing, and terracing. By lengthening the path taken by water as it flows downhill, such practices increase the amount of moisture retained by the soil, thus reducing surface runoff and incidentally increasing the yield of the crop. Not all floods are prevented by proper land use, of course; but it does mean far less erosion, correspondingly less sediment in the streams, and accordingly less likelihood of flooding. Where an entire watershed has been wisely managed after a period of neglect, the change is often impressive.

The Pine River: A Case History in Watershed Improvement

A number of ailing smaller rivers have been nursed back to health through the cooperation of the people who live along them. Among these is the Pine River in central Michigan, which lies in hilly, primarily wooded country and drains about 180,000 acres into Lake Michigan. The main river is 60 miles long, and the combined length of all its tributaries is just a few miles less. The river is 65 feet wide near its mouth, narrowing in its middle course to between 35 and 40 feet. The average depth is put at 14 inches, but during one of its frequent floods it rose to several feet. In 1952 it was described as a "lowland trout stream with deteriorating qualities, with sparse cover on the banks, and with destructive high water." At that time 32 per cent of the land on the watershed was used for crop or pasture, although little of it was suitable for either purpose. Consequently the sand and sandy-loam soils were eroding badly. The rest of the land was wooded, much of it lying within the Manistee National Forest.

In the Pine River improvement program, as in so many community endeavors, one man determined the success of the enterprise. That man was Norman Brown, a land use specialist for the Michigan Conservation Department. Professionally competent, mild and somewhat boyish in manner, yet resilient and determined when it came—as it often did—to persuading a stubborn farmer, Brown was particularly well suited to his job.

After a preliminary survey by reconnaissance teams, a five-year work plan had been set up, with the primary aim of converting the submarginal farmland of the region into forest in order to cut down erosion and the silting of streams. Then, before the actual work was started, Brown went to call on each of the farmers along the Pine and its tributaries, for the purpose of obtaining signed agreements giving his crew access to the land and permission to the Department to build the necessary structures in and alongside the streams. These agreements, which were to be in force for ten years, were not always easy to get. There were times when Brown was obliged to stand outside for

Fig. 51 *1.* A badly eroded river bank before repair is begun (note the three birches in this sequence). *2.* Correction work in progress: the "rip-rap" is laid and the bank is sodded. *3.* The same bank three years later. Photos from Michigan Department of Conservation.

hours in freezing weather if he were to outlast the staying power of a farmer, rather than accept an evasive "I'll think it over and let you know later." Even so, there were a few he could not persuade to sign at all.

When Brown did obtain a signature, he was often able to persuade the signer to join the Soil Conservation District at the same time. After much talk by the streamside about just where the fence and the log diversions should go, the farmer himself might bring up the problem of the "back forty" or "that darn grazed woodlot on the hill." This would give Brown a chance to remind him that it was possible to have his land surveyed for soil types and capabilities, without cost, by experts from the federal government. Frequently, in fact, a Soil Conservation Service official accompanied Brown on his sign-up trips.

Outside events strengthened the hand of the watershed managers when in 1952 farmers came under the Federal Social Security Act, and a number of the older men in the region were able to think seriously of continuing only to raise a few domestic animals and to cultivate a small plot for their own use, rather than earn a living from their land. The Soil Bank program was a further help in retiring land unsuitable for cultivation. Between 1952 and 1958 crop and pasture land on the Pine were reduced by 26 and 48 per cent respectively; now classified as "idle recreational," the area thus retired will eventually become good water-holding forest land. There are now 13,000 fewer acres of grazed woodlot, and over 5000 acres have been planted with pine trees by individual landowners.

Behind the improvement program had been the original goal of maintaining and improving the trout streams of the Pine River watershed (Figures 51, 52). This goal is evidently being accomplished. At the same time, erosion has been largely checked, and the use of the land is more nearly in keeping with its inherent capabilities than at any time since the area was first settled. The people have begun to see the watershed as an organic unit and to realize that they are all responsible for it. They have found much private satisfaction, as well as civic pride, in their work together,

Fig. 52 Streamflow receives attention in stream improvement work: log deflectors are stabilized with large stones. Photo from Michigan Department of Conservation.

and in having made their hills, valleys, and streams more beautiful.

Dams and Reservoirs

Despite the importance of wise land use in preventing floods, they remain a natural phenomenon throughout much of the world. In frequency and severity, however, there are notable differences even in comparable latitudes. In western Europe, for instance, the influence of the Gulf Stream tends to produce moderate temperatures and to distribute gentle rains over a considerable part of the year. As a result, floods are relatively rare in England, Denmark, southern Sweden, and Norway. The American Midwest, coinciding roughly with the watershed of the Mississippi and Missouri rivers, presents a marked contrast. When Marquette and Joliet descended the Mississippi in 1673, at the mouth of the Missouri they were met by an appalling sight. A torrent of yellow mud rushed furiously into the placid blue current of the Mississippi, sweeping along bushes and uprooted trees and producing whirlpools of such violence that the explorers barely escaped being capsized. Marquette, by then a seasoned traveler who had been through much wild country and encountered many wild Indians, declared that he had never in his life met with anything more terrifying.

Such swollen waters, which may occur at almost any time of the year, are the product of a climate in which the fluctuations of temperature and rainfall are much more extreme than in western Europe. Over the central plains the warm, humid air moving up from the Gulf of Mexico and the Caribbean meets with cold air moving down from northern Canada; and frequent tornadoes, cloudbursts, hailstorms, and sudden thunder showers are the result.

For reasons connected with global climatic changes which are not yet well understood, the rainfall from year to year and from decade to decade is extremely variable in the Midwest. Between 1930 and 1940, for instance, in the middle and lower Mississippi Valley even dry-farm crops failed for lack of moisture. The grazing ranges could sustain hardly a fraction of the herds they had supported during the preceding "normal" years, and tons of soil blew away during the harrowing years of the Dust Bowl. From 1940 to 1950 conditions were reversed, and the climate was abnormally wet. In 1951 the average annual amount of rain—thirty inches—had already fallen by mid-July. Around Manhattan, Kansas, thirty-five inches fell in May and June alone. By the end of June the rivers were well above flood stage, with inundations in some places, and cities anxiously patrolled their levees and flood walls. The first days of July brought fair weather, and the rivers returned to their beds. But on July 9 came another torrential rain, in places amounting to seven inches within twenty-four hours. Its fury was spent only after a climaxing cloudburst whose aftermath throughout the Kansas River valley was a flood that cost the nation over a billion dollars in aggregate damage.

Although much catastrophic damage has been averted by the building of dykes, dams, and reservoirs for storing excess water, the slowing down of floods by these means is in itself only a temporary measure. Since all flowing water carries silt and debris that are dropped when the current slows down, any reservoir must sooner or later fill up with sediment. For example, a small reservoir built in 1927 at Spring Lake, Illinois has been found to be filling with silt at a rate of 2.3 per cent per year, and it is estimated that by 1987 the filling will be complete.

For very large reservoirs, such estimates are difficult to obtain. Lake Mead behind Hoover Dam on the Colorado River, a huge reservoir 115 miles long and with a depth in places of more than 600 feet, is an example. Before it was built, there were estimates that 224 million tons of sediment a year would be carried into it by the Colorado. How these sediments would be distributed—specifically, how much would be carried into the lake's outlet arm—was less easily predicted. As it turned out, a portion of the water, which at least during certain seasons amounted to almost the entire inflow, traveled in the old river bed without mixing with the water of the lake itself. As a result, sediments had soon accumulated at a depth of more than a hundred feet immediately above the dam. The question then naturally became, How long before the entire reservoir fills up?

In answer to this question, a technical paper in the Transactions of the American Geophysical Union estimated that it would be almost five hundred years before Lake Mead's storage capacity was entirely used up. But this statement was immediately qualified by another, which puts in a nutshell the problem of all big reservoirs: "The useful capacity of the lake will have been reduced to a considerable extent long before that time, unless other storage works are constructed upstream from Hoover Dam before the operating volume is reduced to any important extent."

Just such new dams have been or will be added to those already built on many rivers—as for example on the Columbia and its tributaries, where thirty-eight storage projects now exist and forty others have been authorized, licensed, or recommended, or are being studied. When the day comes that all these dams have been erected and their reservoirs in turn have silted in, flood control in the Columbia basin will be forced to rely almost entirely on watershed protection.

In the meantime, the interlocking problems of land management and flood control in the United States have become the subject of controversy between two powerful government agencies. Large dams, on the one hand, are under the direction of the Army Corps of Engineers; and headwater improvements, on the other, are the province of the U.S. Department of Agriculture. Critics of the Engineers have accused them of empire-building and of neglecting such important aspects of downriver protection against floods as the zoning of flood plains. Since zoning of this sort would involve the relocation of industries and other drastic steps, as well as some local and regional sharing of the costs, the neglect is understandable. Another question put by critics of the Engineers concerns the ratio of cost to benefit in some of the largest flood control projects.

Historically, the Department of Agriculture has been concerned with land use, the control of erosion, and the increase of crop yields by better land management. As gradually its program expanded to encompass the building of relatively small upstream reservoirs for local flood control, the Department also came under the accusation of empire-building. Just where the responsibility of one government agency ends and that of another begins, remains a matter of controversy—as does the question of the extent to which many upstream reservoirs may reduce the need for one big dam farther downriver. But the controversy does point up one fact—namely that to divide a river basin into upstream and downstream regions is not the best way of dealing with its problems. A far more satisfactory solution would be to treat it as a unit composed of various tributary watersheds, controlled by an aggregate of interlocking local authorities.

The Tennessee Valley Authority

The Tennessee River is one of the few in the world, and certainly the only one of its magnitude, to be managed and controlled as a unit and by large-scale rather than by piecemeal and stopgap planning. Known for its past flood damage and for having had a vast amount of wasted power, the Tennessee with its tributaries drains a total of 26 million acres—an area four-fifths the size of England. Its headwaters flow from the wooded slopes of the Appalachians past such towns as Asheville and Knoxville, to form a broad river—America's fifth largest—that meets the Ohio at Paducah, Tennessee. The streamflow of the river has its mean at 65,000 cubic feet per second, but has ranged from a minimum 24-hour flow of 4500 cubic feet per second to a maximum of 500,000 cubic feet. The mean annual rainfall in the valley is relatively high (52 inches), and there are frequent storms and thundershowers over much of its extent.

The godfather but not the originator of a watershed-wide river development, and with it of flood control in the Tennessee Valley, was Franklin D. Roosevelt. The basic idea, though, goes back two generations earlier to when Gifford Pinchot, an American forester trained in Europe, and the geologist W. G. McGee had joined with the earlier President Roosevelt to initiate the conservation movement. One of their statements read: ". . . a river is essentially a unit from its source to the sea and ought to be developed for all the uses of the waters and benefits to be derived from their control."

Decades later, Senator Norris of Alabama, after whom one of the TVA dams and reservoirs is named, introduced a total of eight bills in successive sessions of Congress, all in some way connected with the management of the Tennessee. The eighth and last, in 1933, became the TVA Act. The remarkable features of the Authority are that it is an autonomous federal agency combining under one roof, and close to the site where the problems lie, the professional competence and interests of diverse federal agencies such as the Army Corps of Engineers, the Department of Agriculture, the Fish and Wildlife Service, and still others whose headquarters and therefore whose site of major decisions are normally in Washington.

When the Authority was set up it was expected to achieve a maximum amount of flood control, maximum navigation development in the Tennessee River, and a large production of electric power, consistent with navigation and flood control. The Authority was also to bring about the proper use of marginal lands, proper reforestation of those lands in the drainage that were suitable for it, and last but not least, the economic and social well-being of the people living in the river basin.

The strategy to achieve all these goals called for large dams as well as local reforestation programs, for demonstration farms and bookmobiles to remote villages, for rural electrification and malaria control; but above all it called for partnership and cooperation with local and state agencies. Some of the goals have been achieved; others are well within reach; and the changes in what used to be a poorly developed or even backward part of America are impressive. Flood control programs have reduced wave crests from two to three feet outside the valley, downstream on the Ohio and even on the Mississippi; further, control programs protect six million acres of agricultural land, and reduce the frequency of flooding on an additional four million acres. To take just one example from the valley itself, the city of Chattanooga during the first fifteen years of the Authority's existence, is estimated to have been spared floods which would have wrought a damage amounting to almost 50 million dollars.

During the same period, with the completion of a nine-foot navigation channel to Knoxville, freight transport on the river increased at least fifteenfold over what it had been before. One of the most immediate benefits of the integrated development of the Tennessee River, however, was the increase in available electric power: in 1933 barely 3 per cent of the farms in the valley had electricity; fifteen years later more than 85 per cent of the farms were electrified. This development alone is believed to have contributed most to the economic recovery of the region, where the per capita income has risen more rapidly than in many other areas and where by 1950 retail sales had risen at a rate that was one-third greater than for the nation as a whole.

Flood control, the production of electricity, and in some cases navigation, are compatible goals of multipurpose dams and reservoirs. Thirty such dams are now in operation in the valley, nine on the main stream and the rest on the principal tributaries. They have turned the Tennessee River system into a series of interlocking lakes that provide enough storage capacity to have brought about the greater

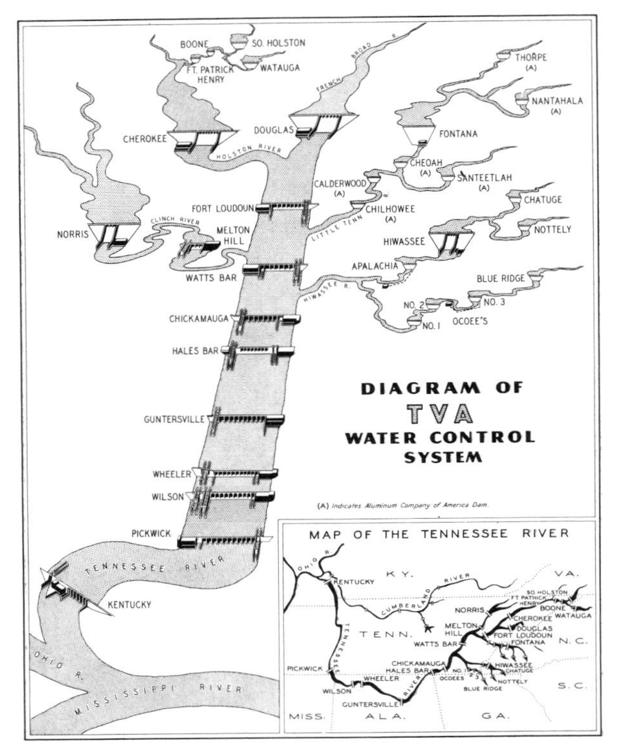

FIG. 53 Diagram of TVA water control system. Photo from Tennessee Valley Authority.

part of the spectacular flood control results mentioned earlier (Figures 53, 54).

Not all flood problems are solved with multipurpose dams, however. Take, for example, First Creek, within the city of Knoxville, which drains an area of only twenty square miles but is often subject to flooding as a result of the brief but violent storms that are frequent in the region. Damage is becoming increasingly serious as the city spreads and as industries become established along the shores of the creek. TVA only contributes advice and technical assistance

Fig. 54 Fontana Dam on the Little Tennessee River; this TVA project combines recreation benefits with power production and headwater control. Photo from Tennessee Valley Authority.

on possible means of flood control there; plans for dams and levees must be executed and implemented by the local government.

The same is true of small rural watersheds where the Authority has assisted in the development of intensive pilot experiments to discover the most effective administrative and cooperative methods of getting landowners and public agencies to adopt, voluntarily, a unified program for the development of agriculture, forestry, and other resources of a particular area. Reforestation, good soil conservation practices, and proper land use are the keys to healthy stream conditions because they reduce erosion and prevent rapid runoff. It was clear that farmers should be brought to take these remedial measures on a voluntary basis; therefore they received free special education and free trips to demonstration farms. The more farmers practiced good water conservation methods, the less became the threat to the reservoirs below, and the longer they would last without silting in.

Water retention measures on the land have long-range effects once they are implemented, but when a serious flood threatens because of unusually high rainfall, the coordinated management of water storage in the various reservoirs is still of paramount importance. The Authority has a central flood office in Knoxville which controls the opening and closing of flood gates on the reservoirs up and down the river. Each dam reports by teletype its water level, discharge, and rainfall, which are then correlated with regularly received weather forecasts. Nine other special TVA offices, geographically spread about the valley, also report rainfall and river-stage data. Proper discharge figures for each reservoir are computed several times a day, and the chief engineers at various dams are informed about the measures they should take. Attention is also given to more specific questions. For example, when the Red Cross is evacuating families in a tributary valley, its officials are given an estimate of how much higher the water might go. Cotton warehouses downstream need additional time for sandbagging before further increases in flow can be made. A farmer below a dam has fifty pigs on an island; a rise of another foot will drown them. Can further increases be stopped until he can have them removed?

Centralized flood management, with its integrated flood control plan, was able to cope with many minor and all major flood problems. Barring hitherto unrecorded rain intensities and duration, the Authority has carried out one of its primary mandates successfully; since it came into being no major flood disaster has beset the Tennessee Valley.

Because the Authority represents a unique way of controlling a river it attracts many foreign visitors, who come to learn more about integrated river development and planning. They usually leave impressed, even though at home the TVA plan has drawn some sharp criticism. TVA has been accused of being a heavy-handed super-state, of being an opponent of private enterprise, of unfair competition with private hydropower interests, and of hampering the development of state programs in agriculture, forestry, and water control. These arguments can be countered with statistics, all of which incidentally show that conditions in the valley have improved since 1933.

It has been speculated by some that an equal degree of development would have taken place without the Authority, which has prevented private enterprise from realizing the kind of development it would have been capable of initiating. Such arguments are as hard to prove as the proposition that tribal rain dance was in fact the cause of the downpour that followed it. What is incontrovertible, though, is that the people in the valley have accepted the Authority, that they like much of what it has done, that it is here to stay, and that many of its ideas and practices are, in essence, being followed all over the world.

Fish Ladders

A peculiar problem connected with dams and reservoirs is the obstacle they present to certain migratory fishes, notably the salmon, whose travels have already been described. In some rivers of the world the salmon have already vanished entirely; this is true of the Rhine, where the inability of the fish to detect the right chemical clues from the welter of industrial and domestic wastes poured into the river is possibly the chief reason for its demise. Along the Pacific coast the salmon are dwindling, for a number of different reasons. Salmon runs once occurred in mountain streams as far south as Mexico; that sizable runs are now found only from the Fraser River in British Columbia northward into Alaska is due primarily to the tendency of the climate to become warmer and drier over the centuries—as may be seen in the recession of glaciers throughout the Northern Hemisphere.

But in the more southerly parts of the Pacific salmon's present range, man has undoubtedly played his part in its decline. Apart from catches amounting to many millions of pounds, the cutting of trees, the building of logging roads, the scouring of river beds, the increase in silt loads, and the building of dams have all contributed to making the upstream spawning journeys of the salmon difficult indeed.

A partial solution has been the construction of fishways or fish ladders to convey the salmon over dams. This is invariably a costly project, which is sometimes financed by the beneficiaries of the dams—the power companies and the users of water from irrigation projects—or which, if the dam is a federal one, may be a part of the original budget. Unfortunately these ladders do not always work very well, even though, as an aquatic biologist for the Portland General Electric Company, G. J. Eicher, has written, "There is no real difficulty in moving adult salmon and steelhead upstream over dams of any height presently proposed or built. Proven means exist to move the fish once they are taken into a good entrance system."

The emphasis here on "a good entrance system" is necessary because of the salmon's natural tendency, where there are no rapids, to swim in the main channel, against the strongest current, as it travels upstream. Since the turbine outflow or spillway produces the strongest current, and since the entrance to the fishway lies at the edge of the stream where the current is weak, the fish may have difficulty in finding its way. The solution of the difficulty lies in starting the fishway at a suitable downstream site, often miles below the dam.

On the Deschutes River in Oregon a fishpass several miles long is now being built, complete with a switchback, entrances on both sides of the dam, and an artificial increase in the flow to attract the fish to the passage. Its total length skirts not one but two dams—the main dam, below which during peak power loads the flow stops for a part of each day, and a regulating dam three miles downstream. Although having a fishway skirt two or more dams at once is a logical procedure, it is of course extremely costly, and often the form of the river valley and the distance between dams render it impossible.

A different approach to the problem is to make use of the salmon's homing habit in transferring it to a tributary stream not blocked by a dam. If a salmon is trapped and its eggs are fertilized in such a stream, its offspring will return to it anywhere from two to four years later, ready to spawn in their turn. This method has been used successfully in the state of Washington, and may be useful in other places as a way of circumventing a man-made obstruction. Transplantation of runs only partially compensates for the losses attributed to dams, as the replacement streams are usually inferior salmon habitats.

As if the job of piloting the parent salmon upstream were not enough, dam builders must also provide a way for the young downstream migrants to reach the ocean. The salmon parr go with the current until they have reached the sea. They may go over the spillway or through the turbines, where mortalities are considerable, through scarring and abrading or by simply being ground to a pulp. The newest way around the dilemma is to stimulate a heavy outflow, such as salmon follow naturally, at one edge of the reservoir and to convey them into the bypass or over a special chute constructed on the principle of a ski jump.

The reservoir lakes on the upper reaches of many large western rivers constitute another hazard to the descending young salmon. The young of the chinook, a headwater spawner, do not usually tarry in lakes on their downstream voyage, but go directly to the ocean; however, when a reservoir lies on their path they may stop there to feed for a month or two. They enter the man-made lake in the spring or early summer, when the water is still cold. Down deep it stays cold, while the upper layers grow warmer. As the interrupted migratory drive of the salmon becomes strong again and the changes in their physiology urge them on to the sea, they try to leave the reservoir; but since they are cold-water fish they turn back instead of entering the warmer surface water, as they would have to do in order to reach the river below. Neither biologists nor engineers have yet thought of a good way to help the chinook salmon out of this dilemma.

Man and the Lamprey

Almost the exact reverse of the obstructed travels of the Pacific salmon is the sea lamprey's progress westward through the Great Lakes, a result of building locks around Niagara Falls. First observed in Lake Erie in 1921, it appeared in Lake Michigan in 1939, where this parasitic fish flourished at the expense of native species, chiefly the lake trout but also including some of the whitefishes. By 1953 the lake trout catch—which in 1940 had amounted to six million pounds and brought about three million dollars to the fishermen—had declined to zero. In Lake Superior, where the lamprey first appeared in 1940, its damage has been so severe that the commercial fishery for lake trout has been closed except for certain boats that fish under contract for scientific purposes.

Eventually the lamprey might come into a more natural balance and permit an increase of fishes too small to be attacked, and of those that live in the shallows the lampreys do not frequent. In the meantime, however, it has become so deadly a competitor with the fishermen that much effort and ingenuity have been devoted to lamprey control. The effort started in earnest in 1945, when electric barriers were built in some lamprey-spawning streams. Lampreys are sufficiently different in shape and physiology from other fishes that electric screens can distinguish them from the rest. Accordingly, while the various trout species were allowed to pass the electric screens unharmed, the parasites were guided into traps from which they were then removed and killed. It was soon evident, though, that the building of enough electric weirs was becoming too costly, and that there were many regions where they could not be operated because there were neither roads nor electricity. Besides, even at the best-laid-out barriers some spawners got through; and since each female lays as many as a quarter of a million eggs, a battle using electricity alone did not promise to be overly effective.

Conferences representing the federal governments, the Lake states, and the Province of Ontario led to the establishment of an international commission, in part to deal with the lamprey problem; and the Fish and Wildlife Service began experiments in an effort to find a selective poison that would kill the larvae in the streams. Since it would have to be a chemical cheap enough for mass application, that would not be toxic to man and other animals, especially other fishes, the commission's was indeed a complex task. A research station was established near Hammond Bay on Lake Huron, where over a period of just under two years a staff headed by Dr. Vernon Applegate tested the effects on lamprey larvae and other fishes of about six thousand compounds. Finally, upon trying tri-chloro- and tri-fluoro-methyl nitrophenols—remotely related to insect poisons but not deadly to stream insects in small doses—they were delighted to find that a concentration of two to seven parts per million of the latter affected the lamprey larvae but did not harm other fishes. By 1957 the Bureau of Commercial

Fisheries had worked out a method of dispensing the larvicide according to flow and chemical nature of a stream so that the concentration would neither be too high nor too low. Many streams have been treated since then, and fewer lamprey scars are to be seen on the few remaining lake trout which the biologists have sampled, although the lamprey is far from being under full control. Since stream studies have shown that the larvae may stay buried for as long as eleven years, there are hundreds of streams which must continue to be treated regularly.

The lamprey program in the Great Lakes is the largest aquatic control measure ever attempted; it now costs about a million dollars a year, and to that amount will have to be added another large-scale program for the rehabilitation of the lake trout. It is not known whether the lake trout would come back by itself or, if so, whether it could be expected to recover in less than a century. In the meantime it is likely that the ecological balance would shift in favor of other fishes that can occupy the same niche and eat the same food as the lake trout—for instance the burbot. There is as little previous experience with the natural recolonization of thousands of cubic miles of water by a slow-growing cold-water fish as there was with the population explosion of its predator. Therefore, while the far-flung lamprey program goes on, government agencies are also growing young lake trout by the millions, to be released when biologists believe that lamprey numbers are low enough to give the trout a chance.

Having to restock the lakes with lake trout provides fishery managers with a chance to "improve on nature," since strains of lake trout might be bred that would grow larger and faster than those the lamprey had been destroying. Other strains might be bred with flesh of a higher or lower fat content, and possibly even with different times of spawning. Having to replace practically the entire stock will mean that the improved fish used for restocking will breed true when they mature, thereby propagating their like in generations to come.

The quest for a chemical to eliminate the lamprey has led to research on selective fish control in general. These experiments have shown that even related species of fish may be sufficiently different in their biochemical makeup to react differently to minute amounts of many dissolved chemicals. Anglers should not think, though, that the millennium is at hand. It may perhaps be possible to rid a lake or a stream of certain fishes only, without affecting the others; but the interactions of various animals with one another and their environment are often so delicate that recklessly embarking on such eradications might have unforeseen consequences.

9

Old Rivers—New Problems

Not Enough Water

The average American's domestic use of water now amounts to over 150 gallons a day—a figure higher than anywhere else on earth. If drinking, bathing, washing dishes, flushing toilets, sprinkling lawns, and running air conditioners were the only uses made of the water available, in many regions there would still be an ample supply for even a much larger population. But these immediate and obvious uses are literally no more than a drop in the bucket compared with the additional demands placed on rivers, streams, lakes, and ground water supplies by a technological society. Indeed, a recent article by Dr. Charles Bradley, dean of Montana State College, warns that a permanent water shortage may well occur before the year 2000.

Since 75 per cent of the water used by cities and towns

and by farmers for irrigation, and 90 per cent of all fresh water used by industry—the generation of electricity included—is taken from streams, the importance of moving waters in daily living is obvious. But in fact the demand made upon those waters by our present standard of living is so much greater than is obvious as to stagger the imagination.

If we were actually to live by bread alone, using wheat as our only source of food, Dr. Bradley goes on to say, the water required to grow it would come to 300 gallons a day for each one of us. That amount, taken from the soil, circulated through the leaves and stems of wheat plants, and given off into the air, is necessary to produce two and a half pounds of threshed wheat—the minimum daily measure required to sustain a human being. But in order to produce the milk, butter, eggs, cheese, and meat that make up the present generous diet of most Americans, the amount of water required goes up to approximately 2500 gallons a day. This more than eightfold increase is due to the lengthening of the food chain involved in the production of animal proteins and fats. A mature steer drinks about 12 gallons of water a day and consumes at least 25 pounds of alfalfa; and in order to grow that much alfalfa, 20,000 pounds of water must seep through the plants and transpire into the air.

The figure of 2500 gallons of water a day accounts only for the food consumed by the present-day American—not for his clothes, his car, the refining of the fuel to drive it, the making of paper for the newsprint he scans so voraciously and so carelessly discards, or any of the other goods to which he is accustomed. Taking wasteful production and mismanagement into account, Dr. Bradley has arrived at a total daily water use of about 15,000 gallons per person. The individual's share of the total daily replenishment through precipitation of moisture in the soil, ground water, and streams, according to Dr. Bradley's calculations, does not exceed 28,000 gallons—which leaves an uncomfortably narrow margin for the expansion of the population that is bound to occur. In fact, all other conditions remaining the same until the year 2000, Dr. Bradley believes that only fifty million more people can be accommodated at 1963 living standards if the rivers are to maintain their usefulness to agriculture, industry, and municipal waste disposal.

Some of the assumptions on which Dr. Bradley bases his figures may of course be debated—one important point being that his figures tend to equate water use by agriculture with loss, whereas the moisture in fact re-enters the hydrologic cycle. Hydrologists believe the ground water reserves to be the crucial quantities, rather than the quantities of water consumed, and they point to regional rather than over-all future shortages. Nevertheless even such conservative bodies as the Select Committee on National Water Resources of the U.S. Senate agree that the water available to future generations is not going to be as plentiful as in earlier days, as well as that we may face grave regional water problems. They summarize the present water situation in America as follows: "While the country is in no imminent danger of running out of water, no longer is it in the enviable position of having enough water at all times for all conceivable uses. In other words, water is quickly moving into the realm of economic goods." An optimist who counted on human ingenuity and a universal practice of the best conservation methods might assert that an increase of two or three hundred million people, rather than fifty million, might safely occur without affecting present-day living standards. In any event, two hundred million additional Americans could very well be a reality before the year 2100, and fifty million more will certainly be with us before the year 2000. The question is simply how soon the inevitable is likely to occur; and it may be that the impending pressure on rivers, streams, and lakes, not less than upon the land itself, will force a decision to regulate the rate of increase in population.

Few people plan for the year 2000, close at hand though it already is. But there are already regions—notably southern California, the upper Rio Grande and Pecos River basins, and the Colorado River region, where rainfall is scarce, and where the rivers do not carry enough water for present demands, let alone future ones (Figure 55). With billions of gallons of water being transported in artificial channels

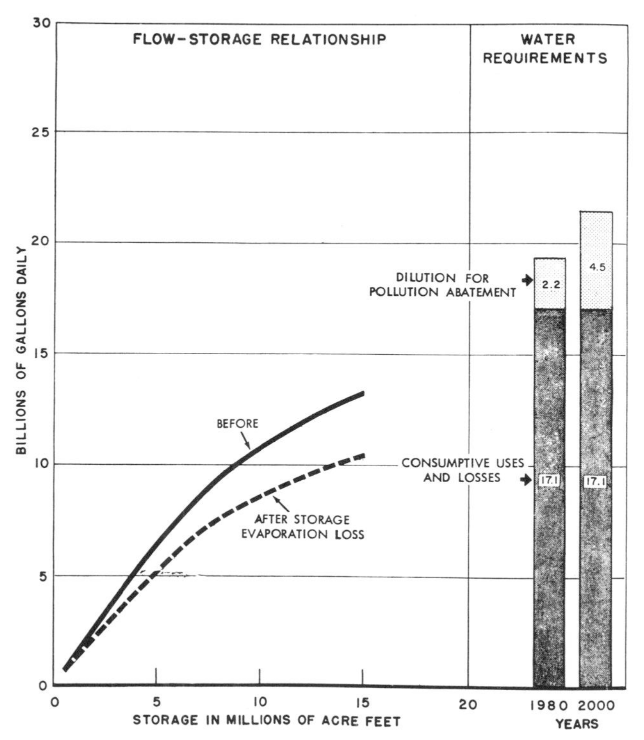

FIG. 55 Present and future water use in the Colorado region. Even now there is not enough water in the river for all uses. (From Select Committee Reports on Water Resources, U.S. Senate.)

for hundreds of miles, the competition for water has led to extended litigation between Arizona and California over the water each state may withdraw from the Colorado River.

In 1928 the states bordering the Colorado formed a compact "to provide for the equitable division and apportionment of the use of the waters of the Colorado River system." With southern California growing at a faster rate than any of the surrounding areas, it is not surprising that California's judgment as to what constitutes an equitable division differs from that of Arizona, and that experts in both states sincerely disagree not only as to who should have how much but also as to how much water can safely be withdrawn from the river altogether. The amounts of water involved here are so enormous that they are usually expressed in acre-feet, one acre-foot being the equivalent of 325,828 gallons of water. Arizona claims, for instance, that over two and a quarter million acre-feet of water a year are available for her use from the Colorado above the mouth of the Gila River, which cannot benefit California. California insists, on the contrary, that Arizona should not be allowed to claim even a half million acre-feet, and that most of the difference should naturally fall to California. Presumably both groups of water experts base their judgments on the same federal data on rainfall and stream flow; and since billions of gallons of water and millions of dollars in potential benefits are involved, there is no wonder that the case should have reached the Supreme Court. Since the beginning of the litigation in 1931, a succession of impartial experts have been called in to examine the claims of both parties and to prepare background documents for the judges. The case has now been settled in Arizona's favor, anticipating the needs of her growing population; but meanwhile the people of southern California already need more water than the flow of the entire Colorado can supply.

Water Laws

Unfortunately, the laws that might have provided the Supreme Court with some guidance in the Colorado River case have not yet been written. The existing water laws deal with man's use of streams, rivers, and subsurface watercourses on a much smaller scale than the present one; they simply have not changed fast enough to keep up with the rapid change in living conditions. The average urban or suburban American who turns on his faucet is aware that he must pay for his water directly or indirectly, but knows little or nothing of the laws governing the use and distribution of water—laws that are as old as those that deal with the ownership of land and other earthly possessions, and no less important.

The first laws pertaining to streams and rivers, containing records of citizens' duties with regard to irrigation water, go back to the early civilizations of Assyria and Babylonia. For us, however, the most important ancient water laws are those of Rome, since they have shaped the water laws of Europe and, in turn, those of the United States. The Romans already recognized a distinction between public and private waters, and even enforced the maintenance of both the quantity and the quality of flow in the former. It was likewise encoded in Roman law that a citizen could take water for his household and cattle and—according to the so-called riparian doctrine—that a proprietor of a private stream or lake owned the water as well as the bed of a stream or lake.

The water laws of the eastern United States, where—as in western Europe—rainfall normally exceeds evaporation, were also based on the riparian doctrine, so that the owner of a streamside property had exclusive rights to make what was called "natural use" of the water, even on a public or navigable stream. Until a few short decades ago water from streams and rivers was primarily taken for domestic and culinary purposes, agriculture, and domestic animals—the purposes originally understood by the term "natural use." Water was plentiful enough so that—contrary to the situation today—following the law's further requirements of undiminished quantity and unimpaired quality presented no problems. There have been some reinterpretations of the absolute rights implicit in the riparian doctrine, so that although the owner of a stream or river property normally has prior rights to the water, he is obliged to recognize that when shortages occur, cities and towns have certain priorities of their own. But such changes as have been made have not been sufficient to keep up with the growth of the population and the requirements of industry.

To the west of the 97th meridian, water is scarce and evaporation exceeds rainfall. In the eyes of the settlers there, to let the water in a river or an artesian spring go to waste was almost a crime. In consequence there arose the doctrine of prior appropriation. In the West the state ordinarily holds title to all water, and individuals can appropriate it on a basis of first in time, first in right. Rights to the use of water must be applied for; they can change hands quite apart from the land on which the water flows, and, in sharp distinction to an Eastern water owner's more permanent and absolute rights, they are forfeited by non-use. Some of these tenets would appear to have had a bearing on the Colorado River case.

Laws are among the slowest of human institutions to yield to change. It has been said that their conservative character is beneficial in serving as a brake against headlong mistakes. But when laws are based on outdated situations and inadequate information, in an area where rapid changes occur, that same conservative characteristic of any one law can also be detrimental. Although much still remains to be known about the hydrologic cycle, makers of water laws in the past knew far less than is known today concerning such things as transpiration, ground water, and the climatic shifts that have so crucial an effect on water supply. There was little recognition by early lawmakers that administrative units—townships, counties, and even states—rarely, if ever, correspond to hydrologic realities. The fact was recognized by the states along the Colorado when they formed a compact to deal with their water problems, but even there the problems are still severe. Although most man-made boundaries are contained within natural river basins and water could be apportioned according to hydrologic facts, matters may be aggravated when two cities or counties that are contestants for water are not aware that an incipient overdraft of a ground water supply has occurred, perhaps because it has been obscured by a few wet years. Indeed, long-term hydrologic records which would allow the setting of realistic quotas of withdrawal are practically nonexistent.

The way in which water laws vary with differing climatic and hydrologic conditions is well shown in the case of diffuse surface water—that is, water accumulated on the land rather than in a defined watercourse, usually as the result of heavy rains. In the humid East, diffuse surface water usually exists only under flood conditions. In Ohio, for instance, property owners may legally apply to it the "common enemy" doctrine, which permits them to exclude the "invader" from their land by any means they see fit, even to the extent of damaging adjoining property without being held liable. Other eastern states have laws permitting similar measures. In the West, however, diffuse surface water is far from being an enemy. In Texas it is considered part of the land on which it occurs. It thus becomes the property of the landowner, who is permitted by law to retain it for his use—although if all landowners exercised this right, serious reductions in stream-flow might well occur. Here the question is not only who owns what portion of the water but also at what time the right of ownership is to be exercised. Whatever diffuse surface water is not promptly retained soon infiltrates the soil and becomes ground water. It is then subject to the doctrine of prior appropriation, and can benefit the landowner only if he already has a well claim there.

An instance of legal disregard for hydrologic facts is in the concept of "defined underground streams," which are a rarity outside such works of the imagination as Dante's *Inferno*. Rather than flowing through caverns, underground water is confined to aquifers, and moves very slowly through strata of porous rock or gravel, which are generally very much larger in cross section than the area occupied by any stream. Thus, though ground water occurs in well-defined channels, its behavior has so little resemblance to that of a surface stream that laws based on the peculiar nature of water in aquifers would obviously be desirable.

Although it is clear that the water laws of the future must vary regionally to fit varying hydrologic conditions, certain trends now emerging indicate how stream, river, and underground water use might be regulated in the future. The riparian doctrine will undoubtedly become obsolete, and the concept behind the prior appropriations doctrine, namely that all water is public property, will take its place. However, the priority of appropriation will be based on the public interest rather than on the "first in time, first in right" principle now in effect in many western states. These revisions will mean that no water rights will be granted in perpetuity, but rather that they will be reviewed from time to time.

Future regulations must also deal with the apportionment of river waters for industrial use. A manufacturer of finished paper, for example, requires 39,000 gallons of water per ton; most steel plants now use over 50,000 gallons, and a viscose rayon plant between 100,000 and 200,000 gallons per ton of their respective products. Laws such as are now in effect, requiring the effluents from such plants to be treated to restore the quality of the water, are not enough; it is obvious that the industrial processes themselves must change if present-day living standards are to be maintained for a vastly increasing population. That such changes are possible has been demonstrated at the Fontana steel plant in Utah, which has reduced its consumption of water to 1300 gallons per ton of steel. Similar voluntary reductions will be made by many industries, but future laws will probably set water quotas for all the major industrial processes.

Furthermore, future regulations of water use will have to take into account all links of the hydrologic cycle in an entire region, so that the whole of a watershed can be managed as a unit. The management may be either by an agency of the public utility type, operating at a profit under government license, or under direct state or federal control. In either instance, political boundaries will of necessity be transcended in favor of the natural boundaries of the river basin or watershed.

Planning on such a scale calls for the resolution of such conflicts as those between electric power interests and the preservation of the runs of migratory fishes. The larger the river, the greater the number of such conflicts that must be resolved before any agreement on the integrated use of the river can be reached. On the other hand, planning for a relatively undeveloped tropical river such as the Mekong is likely to be easier than it is for the Missouri, for example.

The goals of river-basin planning are more easily agreed upon than the strategy for reaching them. It is clear, however, that navigation, flood control, and many other elements can be handled only by federal agencies with large financial reserves and the necessary technical manpower to draw upon. Safeguards against pollution are now moving into the same category. An example is Public Law 660, the Federal Water Pollution Control Act, which is prefaced by the declaration that it is "the policy of Congress to recognize, preserve, and protect the primary responsibilities and rights of the States in preventing and controlling water pollution . . . , to provide Federal technical services and financial aid to State and interstate agencies and to municipalities."

None of this constitutes true river-basin planning, such as it now exists in the TVA, since real coordination is still lacking. That coordination may eventually come through the creation of a Water Development Service in a federal Natural Resources Department, or through setting up permanent river basin commissions which will implement joint action and voluntary cooperation among agencies. But with the population density in some regions of the United States already equal to that of western Europe, the need for coordinated planning is beyond question.

Detergents and Insecticides

Along with domestic sewage disposal and industrial processes, future water regulations will also have to deal with the side effects of detergents. Since their introduction in 1932, the use of synthetic detergents has become so widespread that they now constitute 75 per cent of all household cleansing agents sold. Their chief advantage is that they do the job of soap in hard water and under acid conditions; their disadvantage is that even in low concentration they produce masses of foam, especially when the water containing them is passed over a weir or sprayed over gravel filters in a sewage plant. The foam may rise to a height of several feet, sometimes forming large windblown "clouds," which have even been identified as flying saucers. Detergents are particularly bothersome in sewage works on "blue

Monday," or whenever a manufacturer has distributed free samples of a new detergent. At times the foam persists for many miles downriver, and when housewives in a town that draws its drinking water from the same source turn on their taps, especially at low flow, they may find that the water they draw is fit only for their washing machines. In the Marais des Cygnes River in Kansas a study showed that detergent concentrations of more than three to five parts per million interfered with waterworks operations. Forecasts have placed the future use of detergents at nine pounds per capita per year—an amount capable of producing a detergent concentration of from 70 to 100 parts per million, or twenty times the amount that bothers sanitary engineers today.

To add to the nuisance, the chemical compositions of certain commonly used brands—those of the alkyl-aryl sulfonate class—adversely influence the oxidation of sewage, as a result of being themselves incompletely oxidized, and thus compete for the available oxygen with certain sewage bacteria. Fresh-water fish exposed for months at a time to high levels of alkyl sulfonate detergents have undergone changes in blood chemistry and a deterioration of their gills. Recent experiments in brackish water indicated that the detergents might even kill some of the common fishes such as mummichogs and eels.

Biologically "soft" detergents, which lose their foaming action quickly and are easily degraded, would be the obvious solution. They can be manufactured, although the process is more expensive than the one now in use. Since numerous industries are adversely affected by the frothing and foaming of undegradable detergents in the water they take from rivers, there may be legislation restricting detergents to those of the degradable type, and methods of dealing with the more recalcitrant types may be invented.

Unlike detergents, which are a nuisance but not a real

menace to the health of rivers and streams, are another set of chemicals whose impact on river life is a far more serious matter. Rachel Carson's *Silent Spring* has dealt with the insidiously poisonous effect of insecticides on animals for which they were not intended. Since the book appeared, the havoc wrought upon the life of lakes, streams, and rivers by such compounds as DDT, Chlordane, and the various organic-phosphate poisons has become widely known. Because of the grave implications of the subject, no discussion of water problems can ignore the spraying of land areas with chemicals of this kind. A typical case was reported by Eugene Dustman, assistant chief of the Branch of Wildlife Research of the Bureau of Sport Fisheries and Wildlife, at a conference in Minneapolis in 1959:

The Miramichi River in New Brunswick, Canada has been carefully studied for the last decade to provide a basis for intensive management of the valuable salmon resource. In 1954, a treatment of one-half pound of DDT per acre to control the spruce budworm resulted in the loss of 91 per cent of the young Atlantic salmon of three age groups, and an undisclosed number of adults in the treated area. Salmon losses in a nearby stream that was not treated were negligible. The DDT also caused serious reduction in the populations of aquatic insects. Some recovery of certain kinds of insects was noted the following year. An increase in midges supplied food for an excellent crop of under-yearling salmon, but the second- and third-year age classes were greatly reduced in numbers, as were their choice food items—such as the larger caddisflies. Segments of the Miramichi River were re-treated in 1956 and 1957, and the results were much the same as in 1954. Such repetitive treatments (5 million acres in 1957) have largely undone the fish restoration activities of the aquatic biologists, and a decline in salmon runs is predicted.

A second case reported by Dustman is even more impressive: Clear Lake, located about a hundred miles north of San Francisco, California, was treated with DDD (a relative of DDT) for gnat control in 1949, 1954, and 1957. This chemical was selected because studies had indicated that it was a relatively safe compound with a low vertebrate toxicity, and that excellent control of gnat larvae could be anticipated with little harm to wildlife. The area was treated at rates of 0.01 to 0.02 parts per million. Soon after the first spraying the breeding colony of western grebes disappeared. After the fourth spraying in 1957, hundreds of wintering grebes died, and analyses revealed high concentrations of DDE, the metabolic by-product of DDD, in the fatty tissues. Since the grebes eat fish, samples of visceral fat were taken from fish and analyzed. These were found to contain 40 to 2,000 parts per million of DDE—concentrations exceeding the residue-tolerance levels for foodstuffs set by the Food and Drug Administration. Needless to say, control operations were suspended for 1958. The whole story has still not been recorded, and because the entire food chain seems to be involved in the problem, studies are now under way to learn whether diatoms, algae, and zooplankton store and concentrate the poison. Incidentally, despite spraying operations in four different years, larval counts of gnats in 1958 exceeded all those made previously.

There is growing public awareness of these hazards, and methods of controlling pests by chemical and biological means with a minimum risk to other life are being developed. In the meantime, ultra-severe restrictions in the use of chemical pesticides are to be preferred to the risk of permanent decimation of sometimes valuable species and chemical pollution of soil and water.

Atomic Energy Wastes

Another phenomenon of the mid-twentieth century is the use of water in producing atomic energy. Since plants built for this purpose need water, chiefly for the cooling of reactors, they are invariably located by rivers. Low-energy liquid wastes from the British atomic energy plant at Harwell are discharged into the Thames, those from the plant at Hanford in the state of Washington into the Columbia, and those from Oak Ridge into the Clinch River, a tributary of the Tennessee. High-energy wastes, such as compounds of uranium, radium, or thorium, are stored underground. Medium-level wastes are concentrated, sealed and dumped into the sea—a practice that has elicited protests, though since such materials have to be placed far out of human reach there are limits to choice in the matter.

The aggregate of low-level wastes that reach rivers probably amounts to about the same degree of radioactivity as would be found in the air around a site where a one-megaton bomb had been detonated the day before. If all the low-level wastes thus far discharged were mixed evenly with all the water in the sea, the increase in radioactivity over what occurs naturally could not be detected in any sample. In the rivers themselves the diluting power of the water is so great that today's discharge of low-level compounds does not present any direct danger to man.

Nevertheless, it has already become apparent that some atomic effluents must be carefully limited. For example, only a few curies a day can be safely released into the Irish Sea, one of the disposal grounds of the British atomic energy industry, because of certain nearby seaweed beds which are commercially exploited; the algae in therein—like all other living things, both plants and animals—tend to concentrate certain substances taken from their environment. In peacetime the chief danger of radiation injury to living cells comes from isotopes of certain chemical elements, some of which are used by the cells in maintaining organic processes, while others have chemical properties that are analogous to those of the vital elements. Among the former are cobalt 60, iodine 131, sodium 22, and phosphorus 32; among the latter are strontium 90 and two isotopes of the metal cesium. All of these isotopes are digested and built into the tissues of the plant or animal that absorbs them, in exactly the same way as the parent element or chemical analogue would be.

Radioactive isotopes of phosphorus, a ubiquitous element in protoplasm, are a serious hazard because of the way they are concentrated during their passage through the food chain. Thus, the eggs laid by birds like the grebes in Clear Lake, that have fed on organisms living in a stream, will normally contain anywhere from 500,000 to a million times as much phosphorus per gram as occurred in the water of the stream itself. The eggs and bones of animals are, it is true, a special case: the concentration of phosphorus in the tissues of the body is usually lower. But although that concentration in floating and attached algae, insect larvae, and fishes will only range from several hundred to about 5000 times that of the water, the effects of the concentration are not negligible. According to a statement by radiation biologists in the Proceedings of the Conference on Peaceful Uses of Atomic Energy held in 1956, birds feeding on the organisms in a river with the maximum permissible concentration of P_{32} for drinking water would suffer radiation damage, in addition to becoming unfit for human food. As Eugene Odum, a well-known ecologist and professor of zoology at the University of Georgia, has put it, "We could give nature an apparently innocuous amount of radioactivity and have her give it back to us in a lethal package."

Of the group of isotopes with chemical properties analogous to essential elements, cesium resembles potassium and is concentrated in the same way by living tissue, while strontium 90 has the same chemical valence and forms the same salts as calcium. The bone cells, which extract calcium from the intercellular fluids of the tissues and deposit it into the solid bone, deal with strontium in the same manner. For this reason radioactive strontium will be brought close to the blood-forming bone marrow, and ionizing radiation may then impair the functioning of the bone marrow cells or even destroy them entirely.

The hazard of waterborne accumulations of strontium 90 is probably much less than it is from radioactive fallout. Biologists at Oak Ridge have estimated that a man who ate half a pound of fish from the Clinch River every day for fifty years would still have accumulated no more than 12 per cent of the maximum permissible burden of strontium 90 from concentrations by the fish from low-energy atomic wastes as they are now discharged into the river from the Oak Ridge plant. For human beings the chief source of calcium (and thus of strontium) is cows' milk. Although cows may drink from rivers where there is some strontium 90, they generally absorb it in larger quantities from the grass in which it has concentrated as a result of fallout. Luckily the gut walls of both human beings and cows selectively exclude strontium from the bloodstream, so that the ratio of strontium to calcium is reduced far below that in the grass. However, since children's bones use and concentrate elements of the strontium-calcium group at three or four times the rate of adults, the possible danger to those under fifteen is not to be minimized.

Even though there does not seem to be cause for alarm at present about direct hazards to human health from liquid low-energy wastes, and though the local effects on river plants and animals seem unavoidable, it does not need much imagination to envision a very different state of affairs in the future. Whether the time of rapid developments in atomic power production lies thirty years or three centuries ahead, it is certain that sooner or later rivers will be receiving greater loads of atomic wastes than they do today. From a biological point of view it may be just as well if these developments are slow, since time will then be gained for a more thorough understanding of radiation effects and for sane decisions concerning them.

Among current projects in biological and medical research is the use of tagged atoms to trace intricate processes within the cell, as well as the passage of compounds through a natural community. The relations between the members of aquatic food webs have been the subject of laboratory experiments with C_{14}, strontium, and other isotopes. In one of these studies, Dr. Jack Marshall at the University of Michigan set up a series of model aquatic communities, into which he introduced isotopes of strontium to show simultaneously the concentrations of one element at various levels of the food pyramid (Figure 56). He found that the algae at the base of the pyramid—he used the species *Chlamydomonas*—concentrated the strontium at a much higher rate than any of the other organisms in the aquarium community. Thirty-five days after the start of the experiment they were still accumulating strontium, which eventually reached a concentration two thousand or more times that of the isotope in the water. The algae were eaten by several species of water fleas (*Daphnia* and *Ceriodaphnia*), which in turn provided food for guppies (*Lebistes*). In the fish the concentration of strontium on the thirty-fifth day was about 175 times that in the water, largely as a result of the direct uptake of the isotope through the gills and perhaps through the skin, rather than from its food, because another group of guppies in uncontaminated water but fed "hot" water fleas had lower radiation counts. Clearly, radioactive wastes must be considered in the same light as other chemical pollutants, as well as for the harmful effects of their successive concentration in the food pyramid.

Biologists are also following the relatively long-range genetic effects of radioactivity on aquatic organisms. Although the fishes, such as guppies, that are being used pro-

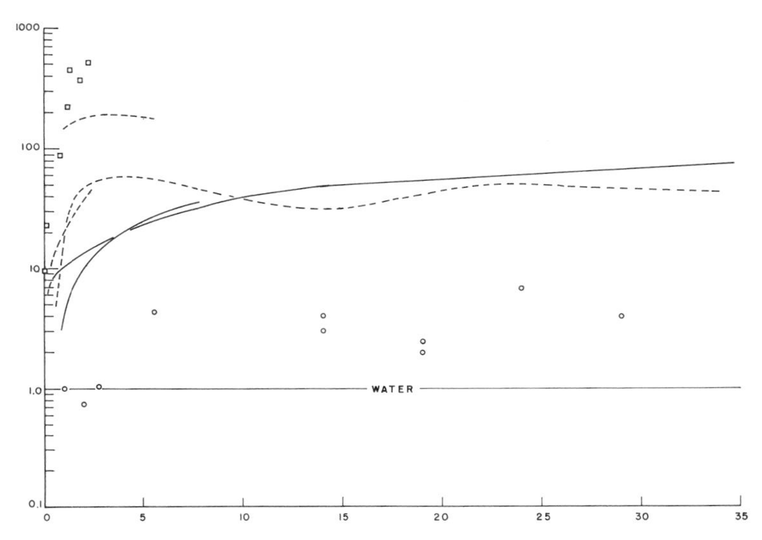

Fig. 56 Accumulation of radioactive strontium in a model aquatic food web. (After Marshall, *Progress Report to the U.S. Atomic Energy Commission*, 1960.)

Legend: *Bottom* = days
Side = level of radioactivity
□ = algae
------ = water fleas
——— = guppies
0 = guppies in clean water, fed "hot" water fleas

duce many generations a year—an obvious advantage for genetic studies of any kind—many such experiments will be needed before any conclusions can be drawn. Estimates of the effect of present-day radiation damage on future human generations still differ widely. But from the figures now available on the genetic effects of X-rays alone, it seems probable that out of the descendants of every hundred million people now alive, anywhere from ten to fifty thousand in every future generation will be suffering from inherited defects due to mutations induced by radiation. Such mutations do not show in the individual whose germ plasm is first affected; and, in fact, since most mutations are recessive, they may not appear for several generations. Consequently few completed studies are yet available on the subject, though in a lake near Oak Ridge the effect of the accumulation of liquid waste products has already shown up in the stunting and the shortening of the life span of its fishes.

Among aquatic animals, bottom-dwellers are more likely than others to be affected by atomic plant effluents because the sediments surrounding them consist largely of the decayed organisms that once concentrated the needed elements, radiation-producing isotopes included. One of the commonest of these bottom-dwellers, the larva of a midge (*Chironomus tentans*), known as the bloodworm, happens to lend itself particularly well to genetic studies. This is because the cells of its salivary glands contain chromosomes that are many times the size of those in the rest of its cells but are otherwise identical—a peculiarity that facilitates microscopic comparison of the chromosomes of specimens from habitats exposed to radiation with those of others from normal habitats. The so-called giant chromosomes thus afford a means of noting induced mutations. In a bloodworm population in the mud of the Clinch River near Oak Ridge that has been exposed to moderate radiation for the past twenty years, the mutation rate has speeded up; under the microscope such mutations show up in the salivary-gland chromosomes as more or fewer black and white bands or in the alteration of the bands themselves (Figure 57). The radiation-induced gene transformations or omissions represented by these differences in the chromosomes may be manifested as lack of pigment, as stubby wings that render the adult midge unable to fly, or as reduced fertility, among

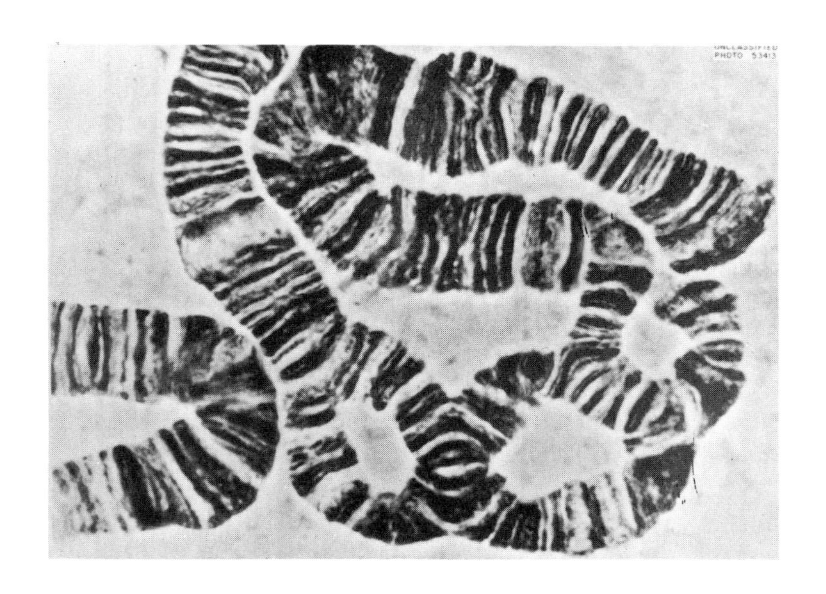

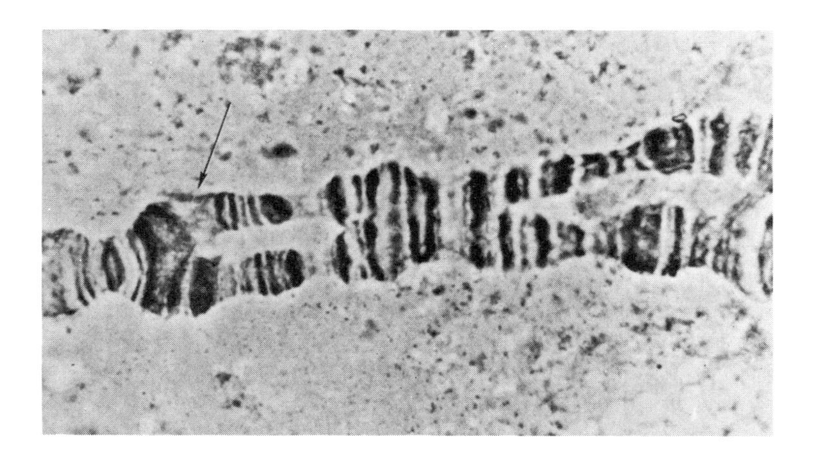

FIG. 57 Salivary-gland chromosomes from Clinch River midges. The rings in *a* and the place marked by the arrow in *b* are believed to represent radiation-induced mutations. Photo from Oak Ridge National Laboratories.

many other effects. In nature the survival of mutants is governed by natural selection. Unpigmented individuals, for instance, may soon be eliminated as a result of being more conspicuous to predators than the normal forms, whereas among domesticated animals such mutations have been preserved and even perpetuated by deliberate breeding.

Although the effects of insecticides and liquid atomic energy wastes are more localized than those of domestic and industrial pollution, all have in common the tendency to eliminate or reduce many plants and animals by producing changes in the water. The fate of the grebes in California, of the salmon in the Miramichi, and likewise of the midge larvae in the Clinch River—however remotely interested in them one may be—are all examples of how, by eliminating a species here, a population there, man has rendered nature continually more uniform and less diverse. Nor is diversity to be desired solely for esthetic reasons. As was shown in the Irish potato famine of the last century, when people perished because their only subsistence crop became blighted, and as became obvious from tropical one-crop economies and generations of experience in forestry, a diversified environment is more stable and resilient than a uniform one. The more variety there is in nature, the more checks and balances exist so that catastrophes, whether natural or man-made, are weathered more easily than where nature has been subjected to uniformity. Coexistence with nature seems no less desirable, if no less difficult to achieve, than peaceful coexistence among peoples. As the human race continues to increase in numbers the tendency will no doubt be toward modifying the natural environment still more drastically, rendering it ever more uniform and ever more artificial. On the other hand, man has been called the master of his own destiny, and his growing awareness of the effects of his tendency will—it is to be hoped—bring about an increasing resolution to curb and retard it.

Streams, Rivers, and Leisure

The time may not be far off when many Americans will work no more than fifteen or twenty hours a week; the rest of their time will be leisure. Leisure to do what, remains to be seen. But since before the end of the present century three-quarters of the people of the United States—who may then number close to three hundred million—will probably be living in metropolitan areas, it seems safe to predict that they will want to spend much of that leisure time in outdoor recreation, away from the cities. What happens to streams and rivers will then be of more general concern than ever before.

Even now, on the few remaining trout streams there is an annual onslaught of city-bred trout fishermen, standing shoulder to shoulder while they try to hook one of the legal-sized, liver-fed hatchery fish which have been placed there for purposes of sport, perhaps only a few days before. Behind this curious development lies an aspect of social history which it may be useful to recall.

In the England from which most of the early North American settlers came, and in the rest of Europe, angling for trout had been the privilege of the landed gentry. Trout streams were managed accordingly, and the fishing pressure upon them, compared with that in this country at present was negligible. In the new nation, wild creatures were declared to be the property of all the people—a concept that was embodied in the laws, which in most of the states early forbade the sale of fish and game procured by those with hunting and fishing licenses. But these licenses made it possible for anyone willing to pay a small fee to enjoy what in Europe had been reserved for a privileged few. It may be the lingering power of association, not less than the ever-dwindling number of good natural trout streams, that confers a consciousness of status and ritual upon the invasion of those waters on the opening day of the season. In any event, the upshot was inevitable: by the 1870's, fish hatcheries were already being set up to replenish the streams.

The members of those early state fish commissions did not know much about the delicate balance among the members of an aquatic community. But through experience they discovered that a stream can be overstocked just as a range can be overgrazed, and will deteriorate in much the same way. Gradually, through painstaking studies with marked fish, it became known that over 90 per cent of a brood die a natural death within the first few months after hatching; that certain fishes occupy and defend territories of their own; and that the carrying capacity of a stream is governed by many factors, including the severely limited supply of food in winter. In short, the practice of stocking a brook or stream with large quantities of trout fry would not automatically lead to an increase in the number of adult fish.

These days, most trout are planted at or near legal size. This practice raises the costs of production per pound, but it also favors their survival during the brief interval before they are caught. A legal-sized trout, by the time it is planted ready to land in the angler's creel, will have cost the state about 30 cents—a cost which is often entirely or partially covered by the revenue from special trout stamps. Planted fish are now scattered along the course of a stream, and at intervals throughout the fishing season, rather than being dumped in one place and at one time.

In an effort to keep some of the sport in catching hatchery trout, the Michigan Conservation Department has tried using Pavlovian techniques and electric shock to train them to shun a man standing beside a stream, rather than to flock toward him as their experience of being fed by hatchery attendants would encourage them to do. It may be that hatchery trout are more easily lured by worms than by artificial flies, since the worms more nearly resemble the food on which they have been raised. And it may be that trout fishermen will one day be strictly divided into those who *must* catch a fish and those who fish for the sport of it. For the latter, only the use of wet and dry flies on a remote, unstocked stream will be satisfactory.

But even today, trout aficionados of this sort are fighting a rearguard action. Their predicament is shown in the changes in fishing opportunities in Wisconsin, a state well supplied with fishing waters of all kinds. In 1900, each of the 330,000 licensed Wisconsin anglers had three acres of water to himself, offering hundreds of fishes with an aggregate weight of about 300 pounds. By 1950 the number of anglers had risen to a million, allowing an acre of water and a hundred pounds for each. By the year 2000 the number will have risen to two million, and the area of water and the quantity of fish reduced by half—with no allowance made for the deterioration of the fish-producing capacity of lakes and streams that may have occurred as a result of the spread of cities and towns with the expanding population.

The shape of things to come may be seen in densely populated Holland, where the angler has about fifty square yards to himself, and where he is lucky if he catches an aggregate of one pound of fish a year—probably carp propagated in state hatcheries. As the pressure on them increases, the available trout waters will be managed more and more as they are in Great Britain, by clubs that lease or buy the land containing them and contribute to their upkeep. The privilege of fishing for trout may eventually be paid for by the pound. Streams may be regularly poisoned out, artificially refurbished, and restocked entirely with trout. The equivalent of fishing pinball machines is more than a fantasy; the author has seen one already. Such things, complete with artificial ozone and pine scent, may one day be a commonplace.

The idea of what is sport and what constitutes a trophy does not change overnight. Yet there are pioneers who try new ways of angling and whom others would do well to emulate. One such pioneer uses the smallest hooks he can buy, with the goal of catching as many different kinds of small minnows as possible in a day's fishing. By means of this hobby he has learned more about fish habits than many an undergraduate does in a course on ichthyology, and has had more fun, one suspects, than many a fisherman with more conventional ideas of what constitutes a sport.

The connection of hunting, a sport in which one out of every five male Americans takes part, with the future of the country's waterways is less obvious but not less vital. If the present quota of ducks and geese taken by hunters is to remain constant, vast new areas of swamp and wetland will be needed by 1980. Yet this waterfowl habitat is declining, and it is estimated that daily loss of water by evaporation in the wetlands equals the yearly water demands of a city of half a million. And, of course, if the projected demand for birds to shoot is to be met, the area of their nesting grounds in Canada and their wintering grounds on the shores of Mexican lakes and rivers would also have to be increased.

Despite the obvious need for coordinated planning where the future of water recreation is concerned, the efforts in this direction have been few and scattered. Most of the public agencies concerned are hampered by a lack of funds; in Michigan, for instance, the statewide watershed improvement program that had led to the recovery of the Pine River has had to be stopped. Among the more hopeful developments is the creation by the Department of the Interior of a new Bureau of Outdoor Recreation. Another is a court decision in Wisconsin which upheld the Federal Power Commission's refusal of a permit to build a power dam because it would have impaired the beauty of a stream now used for recreational purposes. Still another is the recommendation of the Senate Select Committee on National Water Resources that "certain streams be preserved in their free-flowing conditions because their natural, scenic, scientific, esthetic, and recreational values outweigh their value for water development and control purposes *now and in the future.*" (Italics supplied.) A few such rivers—although too few—are even named in the statement.

By 2100, demographers predict, there may be twenty billion people living on this planet. Living space on land will then be at a premium, and vast floating cities will probably have been built on the oceans, where the inhabitants will grow their own food, treat their wastes with sea water, and maintain their own schools and universities, their own museums and symphony orchestras. We can only hope that by then the human race will have developed an ecological conscience strong enough to counteract the pressures that even now threaten the world with a dreary and intolerable ugliness. In a world of twenty billion people there will be many rivers to which today's standards of esthetic and scenic beauty can no longer be applied. But if our descendants are not altogether unfortunate, there may still be a few unspoiled streams where it will be possible to go and sit in solitude.

Whether they are treated as a source of power or as a precious ingredient in a dwindling wilderness, the value of our moving waters is incalculable. In the words of Justice Oliver Wendell Holmes, "A river is more than an amenity, it is a treasure. It offers a necessity of life that must be rationed among those who have power over it."

Bibliography

General Books

CARPENTER, K. E. *Life in Inland Waters*. London: Sidgwick and Jackson, 1928.

COKER, R. E. *Streams, Lakes and Ponds*. Chapel Hill: University of North Carolina Press, 1954.

DRURY, G. H. *The Face of the Earth*. Baltimore: Penguin Books, Inc., 1959. (Geological and geographic background.)

FOX, SIR CYRIL S. *Water*. London: The Technical Press, 1951. (General and geological background.)

KUENEN, P. H. *Realms of Water*. New York: John Wiley and Sons, 1955. (Predominantly about geology.)

MACAN, T. T., and E. G. WORTHINGTON. *Life in Lakes and Rivers* (The New Naturalist Series). London: Collins, 1951.

MEINTZER, O. E., editor. *Hydrology*. New York: Dover Publications, Inc., 1959. (Mainly about ground water, springs, and wells.)

MORGAN, A. H. *Field Book of Ponds and Streams.* New York: G. P. Putnam's Sons, 1930.

OMMANNEY, F. D. *The Fishes* (Life Nature Library). New York: Time Inc., 1963.

Physical Basis of Water Supply and Its Principal Uses, The (Report of Committee on Interior and Insular Affairs, U.S. House of Representatives). Washington: Government Printing Office, 1953.

Rivers of America: series, by various authors. New York: Holt, Rinehart and Winston. (Geographical and historical descriptions of the following rivers: Allegheny, Arkansas, Brandywine, Chagres, Charles, Chicago, Colorado, Columbia, Connecticut, Delaware, Everglades, Fraser, French, Gila, Housatonic, Hudson, Humboldt, Illinois, James, Kaw, Kennebec, Kentucky, lower Mississippi, Mackenzie, Merrimack, Minnesota, Missouri, Mohawk, Monongahela, Ohio, Passaic, Potomac, Powder, Raritan, rivers of the Eastern Shore, Sacramento, Saint Johns, St. Lawrence, Salinas, salt rivers of the Massachusetts shore, Sangamon, Santee, Saskatchewan, Savannah, Shenandoah, Susquehanna, Suwanee, Tennessee [new river], Tennessee [old river], upper Mississippi, Wabash, Winooski, Wisconsin, Yazoo.)

SINGLETON, E., editor. *Great Rivers of the World, as Seen by Famous Writers.* New York, Dodd, Mead and Company, 1930.

Ten Rivers in America's Future (Report of the President's Water Resources Policy Commission, Volume II). Washington: Government Printing Office, 1953. (Geographic description and discussion of economic problems concerning ten major rivers.)

Water: Yearbook of the U.S. Department of Agriculture. Washington: Government Printing Office, 1955.

CHAPTER 1: GLACIERS, TORRENTS, AND WATERFALLS

INTERNATIONAL SOCIETY OF LIMNOLOGY. "The Influence of Current on Running Water Organisms: A Symposium." *Schweizerische Zeitschrift für Hydrologie*, 24: 353–484 (Basel, 1962).

PENNAK, R. W. *Fresh-water Invertebrates of the United States.* New York: The Ronald Press, 1953. (Perhaps the most valuable single reference available on the invertebrate animals mentioned in this and succeeding chapters. It deals with the ecology, general biology, and distribution of each animal group, and is notably well illustrated.)

ZUMBERGE, J. H. *Elements of Geology*. New York: John Wiley and Sons, 1958.

CHAPTER 2: SPRINGS, BOGS, AND LAKES

"Fish Distribution in Norris Reservoir, Tennessee, 1943, Part II: Depth Distribution of Fish Related to Environmental Factors." *Journal of the Tennessee Academy of Science*, 20: 114–135 (1945).

RUTTNER, FRANZ. *Fundamentals of Limnology*. Toronto: University of Toronto Press, 1953.

SHELFORD, V. E. *Animal Communities in Temperate North America*. Chicago: University of Chicago Press, 1913.

CHAPTER 3: STREAMS

ALLEN, K. RADWAY: *The Horokiwi Stream: A Study of a Trout Population* (New Zealand Marine Department Fisheries Bulletin). Wellington, New Zealand, 1951.

FRISON, THEODORE H. *The Stoneflies or Plecoptera of Illinois*. Urbana: Illinois Natural History Survey (Bulletin No. 20, Part 4, pp. 281–471), 1935.

HAMILTON, W. J. *American Mammals*. New York: McGraw-Hill Book Company, 1939.

HARRIS, J. R. *An Angler's Entomology* (The New Naturalist Series.) London: Collins, 1952.

JACKSON, H. H. T. *Mammals of Wisconsin*. Madison: University of Wisconsin Press, 1961.

LEONARD, JUSTIN W., and FANNY LEONARD. *Mayflies of Michigan Trout Streams* (Cranbrook Institute of Science Bulletin No. 43). Bloomfield Hills, Michigan: The Cranbrook Press, 1962.

MILLER, M. R. *The Brook Book*. New York: Doubleday, Page and Company, 1904. (A delightful description of a brook and its inhabitants throughout the changing year.)

NEEDHAM, J. G., J. R. TRAVER, and YIN-CHI-HSU. *The Biology of the Mayflies*. Ithaca, New York: Comstock Publishing Company, 1935.

NEEDHAM, PAUL R. *Trout Streams*. Ithaca, New York: Comstock Publishing Company, 1938.

Ricker, William E. *An Ecological Classification of Certain Ontario Trout Streams.* Toronto: Ontario Fisheries Research Board (Biological Series No. 37).

Ross, H. H. *The Caddisflies or Trichoptera of Illinois.* Urbana: Illinois Natural History Survey (Bulletin No. 23, Part 1), 1944.

Shelford, V. E. See references for Chapter 2.

Chapter 4: Rivers

Carlander, Harriett B. *A History of Fish and Fishing in the Upper Mississippi River.* Madison, Wisconsin: Upper Mississippi River Conservation Commission, 1954. (Deals with mussels and paddlefish.)

Eigenmann, Carl H. and Allen, William Ray. *Fishes of Western South America.* Baltimore: Waverly Press Inc., 1942. (Deals with the arapaima.)

Eifert, Virginia. *River World: Wildlife of the Mississippi.* New York: Dodd, Mead and Company, 1959.

Hoare, William H. B. *Conserving Canada's Muskoxen.* Ottawa: Canada Department of the Interior, 1930.

Nikol'skii, G. V. *Special Ichthyology,* The Israel Program for Scientific Translations Ltd., 1961. Sold through the Office of Technical Services, U.S. Dept. of Commerce, Washington, D.C. (Deals with sturgeon.)

Pearson, T. G., editor. *Birds of America.* Garden City, New York: Garden City Publishing Company, 1936.

Smith, Hugh M. *The Freshwater Fishes of Siam or Thailand* (U.S. National Museum Bulletin 188). Washington: Government Printing Office, 1945. (Deals with giant catfish.)

Chapter 5: The River Meets the Sea

Beadle, L. C. "Osmotic Regulation and the Fauna of Inland Waters." *Biological Reviews,* 18: 172–183 (1943).

Burton, Maurice: *Margins of the Sea.* New York: Harper & Brothers, 1954.

Emery, K. O., R. E. Stevenson, and Joel W. Hedgpeth. "Estuaries and Lagoons," in *A Treatise on Marine Ecology and Paleoecology.* New York: The Geological Society of America (Memoir 67), 1957.

MacGinitie, G. E., and N. MacGinitie. *Natural History of Marine Animals.* New York: McGraw-Hill Book Company, 1949.

Pearcy, W. G., and Sarah W. Richards. "Distribution and Ecology of Fishes in the Mystic River Estuary, Connecticut." *Ecology,* 43: 248–259 (1962).

Yonge, C. M. *Oysters* (The New Naturalist Series). London: Collins, 1960.

———. *The Sea Shore* (The New Naturalist Series). London: Collins, 1949.

Chapter 6: Rivers and Animal Migrations

Adler, Helmut E. "Psychophysical Limits of Celestial Navigation Hypotheses," in Advances in Biology, Vol. 26, *Animal Orientation.* Berlin, Goettingen, Heidelberg: Springer Verlag, 1963.

Applegate, Vernon C. *Natural History of the Sea Lamprey* (Petromyzon marinus) *in Michigan* (Special Scientific Report [Fisheries] No. 55). Washington: U.S. Fish and Wildlife Service, 1950.

——— and J. W. Moffett. "The Sea Lamprey." *Scientific American,* April 1955.

Carthy, J. *Animal Navigation.* New York: Charles Scribner's Sons, 1957.

Hasler, Arthur D. "Guideposts of Migrating Fishes." *Science,* 132: 785–792 (September 23, 1960).

Jones, J. W. *The Salmon.* New York: Harper & Row, 1960.

Oberholser, H. C. *The Bird Life of Louisiana.* New Orleans: Louisiana Department of Conservation (Bulletin No. 28), 1938.

Pearson, T. G. See references for Chapter 4.

Chapter 7: Rivers and History

Bakeless, John. *The Eyes of Discovery: America as Seen by the First Explorers.* New York: Dover Publications, 1961.

Brittain, Robert E. *Rivers, Man and Myths.* Garden City, New York: Doubleday and Company, 1958.

Childe, V. Gordon. *Man Makes Himself.* New York: New American Library, 1951.

Clean Water: A Challenge to the Nation (Highlights and Recommendations of the National Conference on Water Pollution.

Public Health Service Publication No. 816). Washington: U.S. Department of Health, Education and Welfare, 1960.

FORBES, R. J. "Irrigation and Power," in *Studies in Ancient Technology*, Vol. II. Leiden: E. J. Brill, 1955.

STEINBERG, DAVID J., et al. *Cambodia: Its People, Its Society, Its Culture*. New Haven: Human Relations Area Files Press, 1957.

WITTFOGEL, KARL H. "The Hydraulic Civilizations," in *Man's Role in Changing the Face of the Earth: An International Symposium*. Chicago: University of Chicago Press, 1956.

CHAPTER 8: REPAIRING THE DAMAGE

CLAPP, GORDON R. *The T.V.A.: An Approach to the Development of a Region*. Chicago: University of Chicago Press, 1955.

DAVIS, KENNETH S. *River on the Rampage*. Garden City, New York: Doubleday and Company, 1953.

EICHER, GEORGE J. *Fish Protection at the Iron Canyon Project, Sacramento River, California*. Sacramento: California Department of Fish and Game, 1961.

HYNES, H. B. N. *The Biology of Polluted Waters*. Liverpool: Liverpool University Press, 1963.

KLEIN, LOUIS. *Aspects of River Pollution*. New York: Academic Press, 1957.

LEOPOLD, LUNA B., and THOMAS MADDOCK, JR. *The Flood Control Controversy*. New York: Ronald Press, 1954.

LILIENTHAL, DAVID E. *T.V.A.: Democracy on the March*. New York: Harper & Brothers, 1953.

National Conference on Water Pollution, Proceedings of. Washington: Government Printing Office, 1961.

YAPP, W. B., editor. *The Effects of Pollution on Living Material*. London: The Institute of Biology (Symposium No. 8), 1959.

CHAPTER 9: OLD RIVERS—NEW PROBLEMS

ACKERMAN, E. A. *The Impact of New Techniques on Integrated Multiple-Purpose Water Development* (Select Committee on National Water Resources, U.S. Senate, Committee Print No. 31). Washington: Government Printing Office, 1960.

ANONYMOUS. *National Water Resources and Problems* (Select Committee on National Water Resources, U.S. Senate, Committee Print B). Washington: Government Printing Office, 1960.

BRADLEY, C. C. "Human Water Needs and Water Use in America." *Science*, 138: 489–491 (1962).

CARSON, RACHEL. *Silent Spring*. Boston: Houghton Mifflin Company, 1962.

Integrated River Basin Development, by an anonymous U.N. committee panel (Publication sales No. 58 II B 3). New York: United Nations, 1958.

KRUMHOLZ, LOUIS A. "Observations on the Fish Population of a Lake Contaminated by Radioactive Wastes." *Bulletin of the American Museum of Natural History*, 110: 281–386 (1956).

MORTON, R. J., editor. *Status Report No. 1 on Clinch River Study*. Oak Ridge, Tennessee: Oak Ridge National Laboratory (Publication 3119), 1961. (Deals with atomic energy wastes.)

NETBOY, FRANK, and A. NETBOY. *Water, Land and People*. New York: Alfred A. Knopf, 1950.

THOMAS, HAROLD E. "Changes in Quantities and Qualities of Ground and Surface Waters," in *Man's Role in Changing the Face of the Earth: An International Symposium*. Chicago: University of Chicago Press, 1956.

Sport Fishing Today and Tomorrow (Outdoor Recreation Resources Review Commission, Bureau of Sport Fisheries and Wildlife, U.S. Department of the Interior, Report No. 7). Washington: Government Printing Office, 1962.

Water Policy for the American People, A (Report of the President's Water Resources Policy Commission, Volume I). Washington: Government Printing Office, 1950.

Water Resources Law (Report of the President's Water Resources Policy Commission, Volume III). Washington: Government Printing Office, 1950.

Index